Student Haiku & Senryu Anthology

The Nicholas A. Virgilio Memorial Competition

Sponsored by the Haiku Society of America

edited by Randy M. Brooks
designed by Ignatius Fay

Student Haiku & Senryu Anthology:
The Nicholas A. Virgilio Memorial Competition
Sponsored by the Haiku Society of America

edited by Randy M. Brooks
designed by Ignatius Fay

ISBN: 978-0-930172-20-6
August, 2020

Introduction

This is the 30th year since the start of The Nicholas A. Virgilio Memorial Haiku and Senryu Competition for Grades 7-12. Started in 1990 by the Sacred Heart Church in Camden, NJ, this competition has been a collaboration between the Haiku Society of America and the Nick Virgilio Haiku Association. Nick Virgilio was a charter member of the Haiku Society of America and when he died, the Nick Virgilio Haiku Association was founded to promote the writing of haiku poetry, to provide encouragement and support to young people to write poetry, and to further the work and poetry of Camden haiku poet Nick Virgilio. Each year the association sponsors and administers the competition. The Haiku Society of America provides the judges who carefully read, review and recognize the best haiku and senryu submitted. The top selections are published in the Haiku Society of America's journal, Frogpond. For most years, the judges wrote commentaries about why they loved these award-winning haiku and senryu.

To commemorate the 30th anniversary of The Nicholas A. Virgilio Memorial Haiku and Senryu Competition, the executive committee of the Haiku Society of America is pleased to publish this anthology of award-winning haiku and senryu. The student observations, insights, experiences, emotions and insights evident in these haiku and senryu are a wonderful testament to the fresh voices and vivid imagery of young people. We believe the judges' commentaries add a valuable layer of meaning as we see how leaders, editors, writers and members of the Haiku Society of America carefully consider the significance of each award-winning poem. Please note that the short biographies of the judges are from the time when they served as judges.

This collection celebrates the work of students whose teachers have gone beyond the stereotypical haiku lesson plan emphasizing only one dimension of haiku—the five/seven/five syllable form. In these haiku and senryu the reader will find a wide range of form, carefully constructed arrangement of lines, surprising juxtaposition of images, and fresh sensory perceptions. They will find what we all love in haiku—the human spirit responding to the amazing diversity of experiences and emotions offered to us in our everyday lives.

Come, enjoy these award-winning haiku and senryu full of the wonder, surprise and angst that are the gifts of being young. These young people enjoy being alive and effectively share that joy through their haiku and senryu.

~ *Randy M. Brooks, Editor*

Contents

Haiku Society of America's Nicholas A. Virgilio Memorial Haiku Competition for 7th through 12th Grades

The competition began shortly after Nick's untimely demise during a taping of CBS's "Nightwatch" on January 3rd, 1989.

Nick had been invited by the guest host, Scott Simon, who was filling in for vacationing Charlie Rose. Scott had interviewed Nick nine times on NPR in Philadelphia for a national audience. This was to be Nick's his first televised interview.

Shortly after Nick's death, his brother Tony Virgilio, and Michael Doyle, pastor of Sacred Heart Parish, attended a board meeting of the HSA. They proposed a haiku competition for grammar school children. The idea was to commemorate Nick and his unique contribution to American haiku in a way that would have pleased Nick — teaching children to write and appreciate haiku, to enjoy seeing their world through poets' eyes.

Administration and judging of the entries were provided by HSA and for the first year Sacred Heart donated the prize money. The contest still opens in January and closes in March each year.

There were about four or five hundred entries from a few schools in the beginning.

Tony would sort entries at the family home and cull them, passing on qualified entries for blind judging to each of two HSA judges. It was a laborious process with poems for judges on anonymous 3"x5" numbered cards which corresponded with a numbered card with contestants' names that Tony kept. (It is said that Tony provided some prequalifying ostensibly to lighten the burden on the judges.)

Later the competition was expanded to include middle and high schoolers. By March 2015, just before Tony died, we, my partner Robin Palley and myself, received 3,000 entries — 9,000 index cards — from every state in the US and some from other countries as well. Clearly it was time to go digital!

Contest winners, then as now, and their schools are notified and delivered the scholarship prizes (cash awards, Nick's book, *Selected Haiku*, Rick Black's book *A Life in Haiku*, and an NVHA newsletter), along with a *Frogpond* subscription from HSA.

Now ninety-nine percent of entries are submitted electronically — whew! — making processing much easier. We now invited poets to join us to help qualify the entries, remotely via spread sheet, and we accept senryu as well as haiku for judging.

The kids, as you'll see in this volume, explore many aspects of growing up in their poetry

– from love to loss, pets and wild creatures, nature and every aspect of human nature. We see their joys and hurts and realize that haiku and senryu are a universal expressive outlet more important in the digital age than ever.

Here's a point of intrigue: over the past few years at least, in this completely blinded judging, two teachers have inspired a disproportionate number of winners among their students. Again, this year, winners included students of Tom Painting at The Paideia School in Atlanta, GA, and of Arlie Parker at the Sage Hill School in Newport Beach, CA. You may hear them discuss their teaching methods in podcast #45, Haiku Chronicles, moderated by Al Pizzarelli and Donna Beaver during Haiku North America 2017 in Santa Fe. To us, the ongoing success of the students of great teachers speaks to the importance of quality teaching — and of poets engaging with youth to share the art of haiku, the art of seeing the world in a fresh and special way.

It is that perspective that led us to continue honoring Nick's legacy by building what is now the Nick Virgilio Writers House in Camden, NJ. With the Mighty Writers organization, until COVID-19, we were serving more than 100 students a week at the house with after school and writing programs. Now, the home is temporarily a distribution point for food, diapers, school and art supplies — a healthy mind needs a healthy body, Also, we are running a host of virtual programs and invite you all to visit — from mindfulness classes to ginko walks online, open mics to Haiku in Action weekly submissions by our local and global communities.

It took 20 years to make this dream come true: creating a home for advancing literacy, poetics, and the legacy of a haiku poet par excellence. We celebrate Nick and the entire haiku community at the house — home of the Nick Virgilio Haiku Association, 1801 Broadway, Camden.

This house, at a prime five-point location in the Waterfront South neighborhood, is at Broadway and Ferry Avenue across Michael Doyle Lane from Sacred Heart Church where Nick attended mass. He befriended Father Doyle and many parishioners, including myself. It was a nurturing space for him — as we hope the house will continue to be, for all. We have furnished the ample rooms in this 4,000+ sq.ft. building, planted the garden and hosted a Grand Opening with open readings by a host of dignitaries, haiku luminaries, and funders. We then featured the work of poets present and otherwise from the opening in the *Anthology, Writers House Poetry - Volume 1,* available on Amazon.

Our prayers for programming to align with our mission were answered in part by agreement with Mighty Writers of Philadelphia to lease the house and present after school programs — teaching Camden children (3rd through 12th grades) to "think and write with clarity."

We are thrilled to have come this far with the support of the global haiku community. We look forward to welcoming you all virtually at www.nickvirgiliohaiku.org, (or follow us on Facebook, Instagram and Twitter) or at the Writers House.

—Henry Brann

VP Nick Virgilio Haiku Association

The judges for the 2020 competition were Elizabeth Crocket and Michael Dylan Welch.

The following poems, presented in no particular order, are but six out of dozens that made our short list of selections. These poems, whether haiku or senryu, celebrate instants of feeling and perception and share them with readers in momentary acts of vulnerability. As readers, we receive these moments and validate them by recognizing our own humanity in what they each offer. This is what every good haiku does. Thank you to all the poets who entered, submitting a total of 2482 haiku, and thank you to the Nick Virgilio Haiku Society and the Haiku Society of America for the opportunity to serve as judges.

~ Elizabeth Crocket and Michael Dylan Welch

Two scenarios quickly came to mind reading this poem. Was the creaking house a foundation for a scary tale? Or was the bedtime story read to a child with a vivid imagination? The well-done juxtaposition made this both an interesting and worthy winner. ~Liz

This poem's clear and immediate images draw readers into what may well be a ghost story. The poem pivots on a clever use of the word "creaks." Is the verb transitive or intransitive? Normally, "creaks" is an intransitive verb and does not take an object, so we can be satisfied that "the house creaks." But perhaps the word is also being used transitively, taking an object, as if the house is producing a bedtime story. That makes the house especially scary! ~Michael

summer night
the house creaks
a bedtime story

Sahil Gandhi
Grade 8

girl of my dreams
in the crowd
the ball goes through my legs

Gabe Jones
Grade 8

I smiled reading this poem, and if truth be told, I cringed a little too, relating to the strong voice of the poet in what may have been an embarrassing moment. Reading this was a delight, and it definitely resonated with me, forcing me to remember clumsy moments from my own past. ~Liz

For a moment the writer is conscious of wanting to impress a girl, but that distraction causes the poet to miss a ball, perhaps allowing a goal. This opportunity for achievement turns into embarrassment, and readers can feel compassion in sharing such an experience, one that's not just private but magnified by being in front of a large crowd. ~Michael

after my dog's funeral
his imprint
still left in the bedsheet

Julia Kwon
Grade 10

This poignant poem was an easy favorite of mine, capturing perfectly that it is often the little things that can be the trigger for a wave of unexpected grief. It shows great depth in reminding us that life can change quickly, never to be viewed the same way again. Anyone who has ever lost a beloved pet will instantly empathize with the poet. ~Liz

The objects that once belonged to pets (or human loved ones) left after they die create sad reminders of their owners' absence. This image shoots straight to the heart with an overwhelming sadness. That sadness for loss is tempered, we can only hope, by a deep and ongoing love for the lost pet. ~Michael

rainy afternoon
once-loved gifts
in the donation bin

Catherine Dwyer
Grade 8

The first line, "rainy afternoon," sets the mood for the upcoming nostalgia of the second and third lines. It has been noted that Nick Virgilio called haiku "word paintings," which aptly sums up the way I viewed this poem. It resonated with me, making me remember the things that were once meaningful to me that I chose to part with. Well done! ~Liz

The rain is a necessary launching pad for the twinge of sadness of donating once-loved treasures. We see this image sharply, that moment of letting go, perhaps moving on from someone we've broken up with who had given us these gifts. And yet it's the right thing to do, because these gifts, whatever they might be, are no longer loved—and now someone else might be able to love them. ~Michael

I felt the cold night, and I saw the cat lapping the moon in this beautiful poem. It stirs the senses of readers while they ponder the story behind it. I loved the strong image and depth of this artful haiku. ~Liz

We may wonder where the observer is in this poem. In his or her room, seeing the cat outside? Or perhaps walking outdoors when they come across this cat? Either way, we can see the cat licking at water that reflects the moon—wishing, perhaps, not just for the moon but a home to live in. ~Michael

cold night
a stray cat
laps the moon

Gus Critz
Grade 8

The strongest emotions in reading a poem are often evoked when poets are brave enough to lay bare their most personal moments. I found this to be a sweet and touching poem that was made even more moving by the opening line, New Year's Eve. At some point in life many of us have had the experience of not being with the person we dream of, making the poem instantly relatable. ~Liz

The loneliness of kissing one's own pillow is intensified by the timing of this poem. New Year's Eve provides a special opportunity, at midnight, to kiss a person you love when you're together to celebrate the year to come. But here the person is alone, having no one to share that potentially magical moment. We can only hope that the year ahead will be less lonely. ~Michael

New Year's Eve
at midnight I kiss
my pillow

Andrew Reveno
Grade 8

About our 2020 judges

Elizabeth Crocket has had two books shortlisted for the Haiku Foundation Touchstone Distinguished Books Award: *Not Like Fred and Ginger* and *Happy Haiku.* She currently has two Japanese short form books published with Cyberwit.net: *Wondering What's Next* and *How Soon the Colour Fades.* She lives in Ontario, Canada.

Michael Dylan Welch has been investigating haiku since 1976, and documents his published essays, reviews, books, haiku, tanka, and longer poems at his www. graceguts.com website. Michael also runs National Haiku Writing Month (www. nahaiwrimo.com) and co-founded the Haiku North America conference and the American Haiku Archives.

The judges for the 2019 competition were Brad Bennett and Hannah Mahoney.

This year 2,835 poems were submitted by 1,033 poets to the 2019 Nicholas A. Virgilio Memorial Haiku and Senryu Competition for grades 7–12. Poems were submitted by students from 46 states and 9 countries.

We want to thank The Nick Virgilio Haiku Association and the Haiku Society of America for this rewarding and vibrant opportunity. We thoroughly enjoyed reading the entries for this year's competition. These poems were authentic messages from teenage writers, reflecting on their lives and baring their souls.

As we read and reread, and then selected our top six, we were informed by some criteria for haiku and senryu excellence. We were looking for a keen observation of a haiku moment, an effective juxtaposition between concrete experiences, and the kind of precision that is found only in this short form. We were interested in fresh poems with new takes on experiences. We were also looking for depth or resonance. The poems that we selected all lingered in our minds because of their successful craft. Lastly, we wanted poems that represented authentic adolescent creativity and voice. We are inspired by these young poets and hope that they continue to thrive with this form that we love. Congratulations to the winners!

~ Brad Bennett and Hannah Mahoney

This is a deceptively simple haiku with suggestive depths. At first reading, it describes a well-observed moment: the quiet after New Year's Eve fireworks. Then we contemplate the poet's choice of the phrase "year's end." This is an intriguing emphasis, connoting a reflecting back. And the evocation of gunpowder brings to mind the many occurrences of violence both around the world and near to home, making the pause felt at the end of the haiku a hopeful but uncertain one. We appreciate the duality of this haiku, its ambiguity, dreaming room, and possibilities.

year's end
the smell of gunpowder
settles

Spencer Hollberg
Grade 8, Atlanta, GA

sliding home
the familiar taste
of Georgia red clay

Lucas Tangpricha
Grade 7, Atlanta, GA

This is a joyful and comforting poem. The glee of playing baseball or softball on a beautiful day. Rounding third and nearing home plate. Diving into a headfirst slide, going all out to avoid the tag. Scoring an important run. Tasting victory. This experience is also comforting because of the double meaning of home. The familiarity and solace of home allows room for that joy to billow up. This poem is well constructed and slides smoothly off the tongue. This haiku scores in our book!

mountain road
the high-pitched sounds
of spring peepers

Lilly Margolis
Grade 7, Atlanta, GA

This is a wonderfully composed haiku. It includes a lovely parallel juxtaposition between the height of the mountains and the height of the pitch. Pitch obviously refers to the quality of the frogs' musical sound, but also to the steepness of a mountain slope. Both are high; both are intense. This poem also delivers a contrast between the enormity of mountains and the comparatively tiny size of the frogs and their peeps. In fact, the word "peepers" seems to make the frogs and their calls even tinier. Well done!

fence hole
the cat with a nicked ear
slips through

James Propst
Grade 8, Atlanta, GA

This is a sly poem, one that slipped into our consciousness, curled up, and settled in. Perhaps the author is describing the local stray, a veteran of turf wars or cruel humans. Perhaps the author identifies with this cat, still surviving despite the many trials and tribulations of adolescence. We all want an escape hatch, and this cat has found one. Both the cat and this poem are resourceful, sly, and surviving.

twist by twist
knot by knot
mother braids my hair

Lilly Margolis
Grade 7, Atlanta, GA

We were first drawn to this haiku by the lyrical repetition in the first two lines, skillfully conveying the familiar motions of a daily task. It lingered in our minds due to the emotional depth of its image, expressed by the just-rightness of twist and knot. We have a sense of the complexities of a mother-child bond: affection, conflict, understanding, misunderstandings, the parental legacies we rebel against and eventually distill in our own lives. This is a tender and affecting haiku.

The first line of this haiku connotes the restlessness of early spring. The second line hints at a returning, the cycle of seasons. Then the third line hits us in the gut. The literal meaning of fever comes to mind as we realize that the return is not to the ease of springtime but to harsh fluorescent lights, IVs, side effects, uncertainty, and fear. We admire the effective juxtaposition of fragment and phrase, as well as the reticence at work, in this powerful and memorable haiku.

spring fever
back to
the chemo ward

Vlad-Sergiu Ciobîcă
Grade 12, Romania

About our 2019 judges

Brad Bennett is an elementary school teacher in the Boston area and has been teaching haiku to kids for almost twenty-five years. Brad's haiku have been published in a variety of journals and magazines. His first haiku book, *a drop of pond*, published by Red Moon Press, was awarded a Touchstone Distinguished Book Award for 2016 by The Haiku Foundation.

Hannah Mahoney lives in Cambridge, Massachusetts, and works in children's publishing. Her haiku have appeared in a variety of print and online journals, and she is a recipient of the Kaji Aso International Haiku Award and the Kaji Aso International Senryu Award.

The judges for the 2018 competition were Susan Antolin and Charlotte Digregorio.

We were delighted to read meaningful and insightful haiku and senryu from the more than 300 entries we were presented with.

We read many poems that offered a new twist on familiar images and themes, those ranging from nature and the seasons to ones about teachers, family, homeless people, love, loss, grief, hopes, and fears. From the delightfully humorous to the somber and tragic, we recognized the depth of feelings, intuition, and thoughts that modern young people experience.

In selecting the winning poems, we were drawn to poems that felt fresh and authentic. We looked for poems that felt interesting to read even on the fourth or fifth read through the list. Poems that did not tell too much, but which left something for the reader to fill in, were ultimately the most satisfying to read and lingered in our minds afterwards. Well-crafted haiku give the sense that only the right words were chosen. Nothing extra and nothing fancy. Congratulations to each of the poets who won an award and to all of the poets who entered. We hope the process of creating these small poems was enriching and is something you will continue to do!

From reading the entries, we also realized that schoolteachers are doing a wonderful job of teaching the brevity and style of haiku/senryu to their students. Most likely this is because educators are learning a great deal about the two forms from online materials offered by the HSA.

~ Susan Antolin and Charlotte Digregorio

This senryu captures the ironic truth that a power outage can fuel one's imagination. While everything electronic goes dark or quiet, our mind comes alive. Beyond mere irony, however, lies a glimmer of truth. At a time when we spend increasing amounts of time plugged in and tuned out, our imagination may thrive when it has the fertile soil of quiet space. The economy of words in this poem also adds to its effectiveness. Well done!

power outage
my imagination
comes to life

James Russell
Grade 7, Atlanta, GA

**crack of dawn
one blackbird
lifts the grief**

Nadin Ghileschi
Age 16, Botosani, Romania

This haiku is mysterious. What has caused the poet's grief? How does a blackbird change grief one way or another? Does it matter that it is early morning? Has the poet been grieving all night? Often, the poems that linger in the mind are ones that invite us to fill in the details and to ponder various possibilities. We can imagine that here the sound (or sudden appearance of?) a blackbird has attracted the poet's attention and, thus lifted his/her grief, at least for a moment. Perhaps the blackbird is a reminder that the natural world goes on, regardless of loss. The sun rises, birds chirp. Grief cannot stop these things from happening. A beautiful, quiet poem.

**dad
home
without the tumor**

Ben Miller
Grade 10, Newport Coast, CA

One of the characteristics of haiku that is most obvious to newcomers is minimalism. There are very few words in these short poems. And yet, some haiku have an even more stark, minimalist feeling than others. In this haiku, the brevity of the poem heightens the impact of the subject matter. We get a sense that all that matters in the world to the poet at this moment is that dad is home, and that the tumor has not come home with him. No additional words are needed. The understatement of this poem achieves greater feeling than had more words been used. The first two lines, with only one word each, cause us to pause and take in each word one at a time. The third line delivers the real point of the poem, and we, as readers, feel relief. Life will resume with all its busyness, noise and vibrancy, but for now, in this moment, we can stop to appreciate what matters most: health, life, family.

**sewing sky
to sea
the horizon**

Jamie Propst
Grade 7, Atlanta, GA

In just a few words, this haiku effectively captures a moment we have all observed. While the image is very familiar in both poetry and prose, the poet's style is skillful. The verb "sewing" is a strong one. The poet uses it artfully to paint an image of tranquility and calm, melding the natural elements and creating an illusion that we, as specks in the universe, can reach the horizon. The poet demonstrates an understanding of the power of brevity in haiku. The third line, with the two words standing alone, reinforces a sense of awe and grandeur.

If you listen closely, you can hear yourself. Many people don't take the time, but this poet does. The poet understands the human need to separate oneself at times, enjoy moments, and drown out life's commotion. This haiku is both eloquent and elegant, melding nature's grandeur and the wonder of being alive as a thinking, feeling soul. In the first line, with the key word "great," the poet demonstrates knowledge of Buddhism with its reverence for nature, and specifically, for the ancient oak that can symbolize wisdom and strength. Wisdom is found all around us and within us. In the second line, "bask" is a refreshing verb to use in conjunction with "solitude." In the last line, the poet builds to the revelation, drawing us into the contemplative realm, into the poet's heart and mind. The poet has a quiet reverence for the spiritual. The last line's style is notable with the word "thoughts" followed by a comma, creating a pause and emphasis before the revelation.

By the great oak tree
I bask in solitude
thoughts, the only noise

Rebecca Ferguson
Grade 9, Palm Bay, FL

Here again, the image is a very familiar one in both poetry and prose. How many times do we read of the moon hanging from tree branches or branches slicing the moon? But the key verb "impales" jumps out at the reader, standing alone, and illustrating the image perfectly. The poet effectively captures winter's starkness with the barren branch and its eerie appearance, and the awe and mystery of the full moon. It's a haunting scene that stirs our feelings about the mysteries of earth and beyond. The beauty of moon meeting nature allows us to feel that the former—mysterious as it is—isn't so distant to us after all.

the barren branch
impales
a full moon

Grace Ma
Grade 9, Newport Coast, CA

About our 2018 judges

Susan Antolin fell in love with modern Japanese poetry while living in Japan in the late 1980's. She is the editor of the biannual print journal *Acorn: A Journal of Contemporary Haiku* and the newsletter editor for the Haiku Poets of Northern California. Her collection of haiku and tanka, *Artichoke Season*, was published in 2009. She was the featured poet in May 2017 on Cornell University's Mann Library Daily Haiku site, where her work can be found in the archives.

Charlotte Digregorio, author of six books, including *Haiku and Senryu: A Simple Guide for All* and *Shadows of Seasons,* a haiku collection, has won 46 poetry awards, and was nominated for a Pushcart Prize. Her traveling haiga show runs in many locations year 'round. A former HSA officer, and now an Ambassador to The Haiku Foundation, she recently received an official commendation from Illinois Governor Bruce Rauner for her 38 years of literary achievement and work advancing the literary arts.

2017

The judges for the 2017 competition were Linda Papanicolaou and Brad Bennett.

This year there were almost 6,000 poems entered in the Nicholas A. Virgilio Memorial Haiku and Senryu Competition. It is impressive and very heartening that so many students entered their poems. We were especially struck by the range of emotions embedded in the poems, from hope and glee all the way to pain and loneliness. We hope that poetry, and haiku in particular, continues to provide an outlet for these young writers to express these feelings through concrete imagery.

What did we look for in these haiku and senryu? We looked for a fresh and successful rendering of a moment observed, a deft portrayal of concrete sensory experiences, an allusion to emotions rather than personal revelation, simple language, and a strong voice, all of which are necessary when writing excellent haiku and senryu. We were also looking for a distinctive young person's voice in each of the winning poems.

We felt honored to be asked to judge this contest. We very much enjoyed the whole process, from reading the poems, to rereading the poems, to rereading the poems again, to discussing the poems we most appreciated, to whittling all the wonderful poems down to a mere six winners. There were many more that deserved praise. But the final six resonated for us. Their writers showed creativity, voice, and knowledge of the craft of writing a successful haiku. Congratulations to the winners!

~ *Linda Papanicolaou and Brad Bennett*

This haiku very effectively accentuates how oppressive a heat wave can be. The word "endless" is the first indication that this heat has gone on long enough. Not only that, all the basketball player has to shoot at is one "broken" hoop. That's disheartening! The writer, by carefully selecting these words, has masterfully alluded to feelings of loneliness and boredom, perhaps as oppressive as the heat. But we can also appreciate the writer's dedication to practice. Well executed!

In the summer heat
endless jump shots
on a broken hoop

Stephanie Okeke
Grade 12, Gardena, CA

tea leaves
she stirs them
for something better

Olivia Shannon
Grade 7, Atlanta, GA

One of the common themes of the human condition is to want to change our lives for the better, especially if we're struggling with something. We often go to great lengths to shake things up, but sometimes we do little things to make a difference. Like stirring some tea leaves. So, this poem connects with a universal desire. In addition, the unknown subject "she" brings some wonderful mystery to this poem. Is the writer speaking autobiographically? Is it about someone important in the writer's life ... a friend, a mother, a sister? The meaning changes depending on this choice, and that ambiguity gives this senryu added intrigue and resonance.

Amber alert
one desk
empty

Campbell Serrano
Grade 7, Atlanta, GA

A common misperception about a senryu is that it's a humorous poem that focuses on human foibles. Not so—as this poem shows, it can also be about deadly serious matters, and emotion. The effectiveness of this poem lies in its minimalism and its shape, an inverted triangle that narrows to one start word, "empty", on the third line. Rather than telling—or even showing—the emotional responses of the other students, the emptiness of that desk places us in the classroom, feeling directly the unspeakable fear of a child's kidnapping.

our parrot shrieks
my father's name
in my mother's voice

Cole Mitchell
Grade 12, Newport Coast, CA

This is a classic, wonderfully funny senryu. Since parrots learn what they hear often, it speaks volumes about the dynamics of a household in which the mother's and the family parrot's voices mirror each other. The choice of a single word can make or break a poem. In this case it's the opening "our", which sets the poem within the child's point of view and frames the joke with a knowing humor.

father's silhouette
cut from the photo
his hand still on her shoulder

Cole Mitchell
Grade 12, Newport Coast, CA

This is a powerful senryu. The author uses a concrete image, an altered photograph, to allude to some very strong feelings. Why is the father cut out? Is this a "broken" family? Is the father no longer living? Is the girl mad at the father? And even though an attempt has been made to cut this man out, his emotional impact lingers on. In addition, the last line is longer than the first two, and that adds to the lingering effect of the hand, and the pain.

The emotional strength of this haiku is its nostalgic evocation of childhood memories of stargazing on clear summer nights. How many of us have been taught by our fathers to pick out the constellations and planets? In its simplicity of words, this haiku is well crafted, with both cut and kigo ("a million stars" would be a late summer/early autumn reference), and the choice of imagery draws a wonderful contrast between the immensity of the night sky and the intimacy of a father teaching his child that some worlds are not quite as far away as the stars.

millions of stars
my father
points out a planet

Daisy Solomon
Grade 8, Atlanta, GA

About our 2017 judges

A middle school art teacher and art historian, Linda Papanicolaou became interested in haiku and haiga in the late 1990s when she taught a 5th grade art lesson that combined leaf printing and haiku. The leaf prints were beautiful, the haiku not, and she realized she'd have to learn more about haiku. Although she never taught that lesson again, she has become a committed haiku poet who also writes senryu, haiga, haibun and renku. She has published widely and is a member of the Yuki Teikei Haiku Society, Haiku Poets of Northern California, and the Haiku Society of America. For the past twelve years she has edited Haigaonline.

Brad Bennett is an elementary school teacher in the Boston area and has been teaching haiku to kids for over 20 years. Brad's haiku have been published in a variety of journals and magazines. He is a member of the Summer Street Haiku Group, the Boston Haiku Society, and the Haiku Society of America. His first haiku book, *a drop of pond*, published by Red Moon Press, was awarded a Touchstone Distinguished Book Award for 2016 by The Haiku Foundation.

The judges for the 2016 competition were Joan Iversen Goswell and Alison Woolpert.

This year we had over 3,000 haiku to judge from all 50 states, the District of Columbia, and at least four other countries: Romania, Egypt, Canada and Hong Kong. We were excited to see so much student work come in.

We were honored to be selected as the judges for the Nicholas A. Virgilio Memorial Haiku Contest. The criteria that we felt was most important was the haiku's expression, how the words worked together to form a feeling, an insight and most importantly, thoughts it evoked. We did not look for the 5/7/5 syllable form, which can make a haiku written in English seem overly dense, but we did consider a seasonal reference that can add depth to a haiku.

Congratulations not only to the winners, but also to everyone who participated in the 2016 Nicholas A. Virgilio Memorial Haiku Competition. Picking the winners was difficult; we were impressed by the talent, creativity and insights of many of the haiku. We hope all of the young people who entered continue in their creative endeavors. They are off to a good start.

~ *Joan Iversen Goswell and Alison Woolpert*

Under the cover of night, time is suspended. It's summer; we all know those evenings where you just don't want to go back inside the house at all. The growing darkness is enveloping these two, heightening their bond. They continue to play, feeling as if they are the only two people in the world enjoying the sport they so love. You can hear the rhythmic sounds of the ball hitting the bat, then the glove. No homerun swings in darkness, just grounders. The teen has Dad all to him or herself. Dad also has the teen to himself; a teen that he knows will all too soon be leaving home for adulthood.

hours after practice
just me and Dad
hitting into the dark

Connor Brock
Age 18, Grade 12,
Newport Coast, CA

bare feet
dewy moss
between flagstone

Emma Jones
Age 15, Grade 10, Atlanta, GA

"Bare feet" is a kigo. A kigo is what is known as a seasonal reference, and summer is the season. It is a haiku written of a single moment. Maybe it has been a long day of heat and humidity and she longs for some relief. She comes home and takes her shoes off, then goes out in the backyard. She steps on the soft coolness of the moss, and feeling it, suddenly realizes how lovely the day has become. This haiku is of pure sensuality. Just feel it and linger there.

a hay bale
in the distance
the silent horse

Hunter Collins
Age 14, Grade 8, Atlanta, GA

This is a dark, sad haiku. There are hidden meanings of alienation. Is the owner aware of the horse? Does he even care? Maybe something bad has happened to the owner. We don't know, but if the horse could get to the hay, he would. For some reason he can't. Maybe he is in his stall or tied to something and can't get loose. Is the horse sick, weak, or in pain? Has he been neglected without feed or water for a long time? Has the horse given up on his life and accepted his fate? Horses are stoic if they are in pain, neglected, or thin and weak. We find this haiku to be very unsettling. We find ourselves hoping that there will soon be a change for the better in the horse's life.

late winter morning
a broken bench
alone in the woods

Ellie Woodcock
Age 14, Grade 8, Atlanta, GA

Winter can be desolate, and it is the season of the mind. At the darkest time of the year we are more likely to ponder our existential being, the cycle of birth, life, and death. This haiku takes us there. The scene evokes a sense of loss or abandonment. It's very cold outside and there are woods surrounding the broken bench. It is not only the broken bench that is alone, but also the observer of the scene. Is there a split in a relationship, or an illness? The kigo, late winter, can't help but make us think of fate, of endings; here of the broken bench at the end of its life, and that of the observer, possibly someone once young but now in old age, alone in the woods with the end of life approaching, or at least of an observer who is facing an end of some important facet of his life. It is a quiet, contemplative haiku.

There is a mystery to this. There is also poignancy. Where is Papa? When will he return? Will the child be able to do the farm work that Papa left behind? The cracked tractor seat implies that he has been gone a long time. Why did he leave? The child hopes that he is not gone forever and keeps waiting, hope against hope, for his return. This haiku evokes both hope and sadness without being overt. It does not give us answers; it is beautifully written.

cracked tractor seat
waiting
for Papa's return

Ashton Carroll
Age 15, Grade 10, Laguna Hills, CA

What wonderful energy in just 12 syllables! It must be a spring rain that brought this joy into play. What do kids do on a rainy day when there's nothing else to do? Why they make tinfoil boats and sail them down the driveway! You can imagine the laughter while they fashion different kinds of tinfoil boats and race each other. Which shape travels the fastest? Do any boats carry a plastic figurine Captain or ferry plastic farm animals? More laughter is heard as a boat goes down a drain or along the gutter. They are just plain having fun! It is infectious. It makes us adults remember when we were kids having fun. It makes us smile. Ah, the joys of childhood.

tinfoil boats
down the driveway
a child's rainy day

Emma Jones
Age 15, Grade 10, Atlanta, GA

About our judges

Joan Iversen Goswell is a poet and artist. Her first experience with haiku was many years ago when she read the Harold Henderson books. It was a stunning discovery! She decided right there and then that she wanted to write haiku so she studied the greats and stumbled on, teaching herself as best as she could. She has since been published in journals such as *Modern Haiku* and *Frogpond*. Her poems have been included in several anthologies. As an artist she specializes in handmade artists books. She has a strong interest in Japanese culture, Zen art and literature. She also studies Cha No Yu, the Japanese tea ceremony. She lives on her farm with three horses and two Jack Russell terriers and is surrounded by nature which continues to inspire her to write haiku!

Alison Woolpert became interested in haiku as a child, and later, through teaching haiku to elementary students. She is a member of Haiku Society of America, Haiku Poets of Northern California, and Yuki Teikei Haiku Society (YTHS). She served as President of YTHS from 2010-2015. She also writes tanka, haibun, and creates haiga. Her poetry has appeared in a variety of journals. She sees, not sells, shells by the seashore in Santa Cruz, CA.

2015

The judges for the 2015 competition were Mike Rehling and Aubrie Cox.

This year we had over 3,600 haiku to judge. We were excited to see so much student work come in. There were, of course, the traditional 5–7–5 poems along with those that were clearly writing about the fact that they had to write a haiku. However, with that said, many of them delved deep into the psyche and human experience. We were moved by those that opened up about depression, about heartbreak and the loss of family members. We were also delighted by those that captured the wonders of childhood.

In the end, we looked for quality haiku: poems that had a clear cut and juxtaposition of images and/or ideas, offered original ideas for universal experiences, and simply moved us.

~ *Mike Rehling and Aubrie Cox*

We were enamored with this haiku's wit and play on words. It captures the essence of the relationship between a child and a future stepparent who desperately wants the child to like him or her. The first two lines make it seem as though the speaker is bored and that the soon-to-be stepdad is blabbering on about grown-up matters, but the third line provides a twist at the end, showing the reader that the future stepdad is talking to the child but he or she isn't impressed. "Blabbers" works multiple angles and serves an important role in this haiku.

soon-to-be stepdad
blabbers politics
looking for my vote

Elena Bonvicini
Sage Hill School, Grade 10,
Newport Coast, CA

Nothing could be worse in the puzzle world than getting almost there and having to endure the indignity of an incomplete image. This group of puzzle solvers has not resorted to blaming one another or using the worn out "the dog ate it" line. No, they have placed the blame squarely on a piece of metal and plastic. There is a creativity in their decision on where to place the blame that shows they indeed are good at problem solving, if not puzzles.

missing puzzle piece
we blame
the vacuum

Maggie George
Sprayberry High School, Age 16,
Grade 11, Marietta, GA

first day of school
eating lunch
in the bathroom

Catharine Malzahn
Sage Hill School, Grade 10
Newport Coast, CA

Starting in a new school, or a new year in a new building can be tough. We can just imagine a kid on his or her first day not knowing where to sit in the lunchroom and too shy to talk to anyone, so he or she eats alone in the bathroom where there is privacy and not a lot of noise. This haiku does a phenomenal job of conveying emotion without stating that the child may be feeling sad, anxious, out of place, etc. It establishes season and location without any excess words.

coffee crumble cake
my mom
brings up grades

Kian Etedali
Sage Hill School, Grade 12,
Newport Coast, CA

If your mother is going to bring up your grades, chances are you are not on track to be valedictorian of your class. But if you have to endure that discussion it is by far better to do it with "coffee crumble cake" on a plate in front of you. It is a sign of a Mom who gets her way without resorting to brute force, but then again that cake is indeed a force to be reckoned with in the end.

Friday morning prayer
purple hijabs
dance in the wind

Claire Reardon
St. Ignatius College Prep, Grade 12,
Chicago, IL

We don't see a lot of haiku that mention hijabs, which is unfortunate. The way this poem uses specific language and shifts from line one to line two makes it an evocative haiku. There's something contemplative about the fabric moving in the wind during prayer: the movement, the rich yet lightness in the color purple, and the early morning air. There are limitless possibilities for smells and sounds that undoubtedly heighten while our eyes are closed, and we lower ourselves to the ground.

bedtime story
only pretending
to fall asleep

Sophie Sadd
The Paideia School, Grade 8,
Atlanta, GA

As we grow up there is the inevitable pull between the child in us and the desire to be fully adult. Children are not the only ones torn between these two aspects of our life. Parents want their kids to grow up, but they also hang on to the fond memories of childhood, both their own and their child's. In this poem we have bridged that gap nicely. The parent is reading the story, and the child has kindly allowed this to happen, but cut short the moment with their own very kind deception. It shows the merger of child and adult in one fell swoop.

About our judges

Aubrie Cox went to university to write a novel and came out writing haiku. It's worked pretty well so far. Now, she is an editor for both the online journal *A Hundred Gourds and Juxtapositions: A Journal of Haiku Research and Scholarship*. Her poetry and prose can be found in publications such as *Frogpond, Modern Haiku,* and *NANO Fiction.*

Michael Rehling is a quiet poet, living in the North Woods of Michigan with his wife and two cats.

The judges for the 2014 competition were Rick Black and Raffael de Gruttola.

It has been a real pleasure to judge the 2014 Nicholas A. Virgilio Memorial Haiku Competition. We received 793 entries—a daunting number—but we each read all of the poems and then narrowed it down to approximately 20 of our favorites. We then read the final poems out loud to each other and discussed the merits of each one.

Our criteria were as rigorous as they would have been for an adult contest—weighing the overall effect, sensibility, grammar, pacing, and word choice. We were looking for poems that resonated beyond the verse itself or were moments keenly perceived. It was not easy to narrow down our selection and to choose six of the best poems.

Whether or not you were among the winners, we hope that you will continue to write and to plumb the depths of your life through haiku and other forms of poetry. You are doing a great job using words to try to make sense of life and to record those moments most precious to you that you would like to share.

The following are our winners. They are not listed in any particular order in terms of one being better than another. They are all wonderful poems.

~ *Rick Black and Raffael de Gruttola*

We love the way in which the author depicted the close relationship that people and animals have with each other—simply manifested in the sensation of a heartbeat. The acceptance of feeling and trust of this simple moment captures the symbiotic sensation from cat to person and person to cat. It's the relationship that a mother might have with her newborn, two hearts beating in unison. Trust is never compromised.

napping cat
her heart beating
on mine

Marisa Schwartz
The Paideia School, Grade 9, Atlanta, GA

abandoned trailer park
a pink flamingo
on the lawn

Aja Smith-Saunders
The Paideia School, Grade 8,
Atlanta, GA

In this poem, a bird of flight is present while the
people have moved on. There is a poignancy between
the abandoned homes and flamingo, which may
or may not be real. This bird of flight, this pink
flamingo, serves as a symbol that we, whomever that
may be, may not or cannot ever return. For one of
the judges, this poem recalled the image of Hurricane
Katrina when so many people were displaced.

after the beach
five-day-old sand
between my toes

Mariah Wilson
Sage Hill School, Grade 12,
Newport Coast, CA

Sand from the beach sticking between our toes long
after we've left is a familiar feeling for many of us.
The tiny, leftover granules of sand recall a day at
the beach—wind flapping against kites, seagulls,
beach umbrellas, and sun shimmering on waves. In
fact, the author prompts us to remember our own
beach experiences—and the way in which they
have gotten stuck in our own memory.

my Grandma
watching her pine trees
for the last time

Grant Dunlavey
Sage Hill School, Grade 9,
Newport Coast, CA

To write about separation

is not an easy task, but this poem manages to do
so in a poignant way. We naturally get a sense of
sadness even though this emotion is never explicit. A
grandmother apparently has lived in this place a long
time and perhaps is off to a nursing home or another
less homey place. The sense of sabi—of sadness at
parting, of loss and aloneness—resonates long after
our finishing the verse. Of course, we don't know for a
fact that the grandmother is sad? It is quite possible
that she is happy to be leaving this place, and it's
also this breadth of interpretation that we found so
appealing.

her greenhouse
16 plants
he knows by name

Ryan Shuman
Sage Hill School, Grade 12,
Newport Coast, CA

In this poem, one can imagine the devotion to
life that this person gives to the plants inside her
greenhouse. We imagine her rising early, perhaps,
watering the ones that need it or pinching off some
yellowed leaves in the middle of winter. It's the
preciseness of observation that is so memorable and
that particularly captured our attention—not one
more, not one less plant. Similarly, the author has
used not one more, not one less word than necessary.

We like the richness of possibility that this haiku presents as well as the way in which the resonance of a Spanish presence is retained through the original name. While haiku are often about smaller things, they can also reflect the vastness of a landscape. El Morro (as a number of places were called by the Spanish explorers) could refer to a variety of locations, including a California beach, a national monument in western New Mexico, or the castle guarding the harbor in Havana, Cuba. The author of the poem contrasts a sense of history with the palpable sensation of saltwater on a sunburned back—all of which deepens our sense of the landscape as well as our interaction with it.

El Morro
saltwater stinging
my sunburned back

Michelle Oglevie
*Sage Hill School, Grade 12,
Newport Coast, CA*

About our 2014 judges

Rick Black is a poet and book artist who runs Turtle Light Press. His haiku collection, *Peace and War: A Collection of Haiku from Israel*, has been called "a prayer for peace" by Emmy award-winning poet Kwame Dawes. His most recent book, *Star of David*, won the 2013 *Poetica Magazine* poetry contest. Black has garnered several international awards for his haiku poetry and his poems and haiku have appeared in a variety of journals. He was haiku poet of the month in April 2013 at Cornell University's Mann Library.

Raffael de Gruttola, past president and treasurer of the Haiku Society of America in the 90s, is a poet and editor of haiku, senryu, renku, haiga, and haibun. In 1988 he was a founding member of the Boston Haiku Society and the editor of its newsletter. He recently was elected as the 2nd vice president of the United Haiku and Tanka Society of America. His haiku and other Japanese poetic forms have been printed throughout the U.S., Japan, Canada, Romania, Ireland, England, and other countries.

The judges for the 2013 competition were Mary Stevens and John Stevenson.

A jack-o-lantern almost always has teeth and they are almost never the sort of teeth that indicate good dental hygiene. In fact, they are the sort of teeth that, in a human being, would be especially sensitive to changes in temperature and might react to an autumn wind with a twinge of pain. Of course, we don't so much feel the wind as see it in this haiku. It causes the candle within to flicker, falter, and perhaps expire.

The wind moving through the mouth of the jack-o-lantern brings to mind how living beings take in and exhale air as part of the breathing process. The word "spirit," in its sense as the animating principle in humans and animals, comes from the same Latin root as "breath" (respiration). That which is alive, breathes. But could it also be true that breathing feeds the flame inside? If breath is an animating force, the implications of this poem are ghoulish…

A number of idioms come to mind when reading this poem: speaking "through the teeth" and "in the teeth of," to name a couple. This poem stood out from the first reading because it is so well crafted. The line breaks, in particular, are cut in the most expressive way possible.

through the teeth
of the jack-o-lantern
the wind

Addison Owen
The Paideia School, Age 14, Grade 9, Atlanta, GA

family dinner
the lights
too dim

Danielle Murdoch
The Paideia School, Age 14, Grade 8, Atlanta, GA

In any group, there are going to be different perceptions about the comfort level for things like the temperature, the lighting, the music. It is clear that the poet is not the one who decides what the proper lighting is in this family group. All the same, it is good to be clear about this within oneself. Someday, when creating a new family, it will be good to be articulate about it.

Traditional Western poetry often expresses the poet's deepest feelings explicitly. In contrast, Japanese aesthetics values suggesting emotion instead of stating it outright. This can make writing haiku very challenging for Westerners, who want to express and who strive to be heard and understood. This poem does not reveal the storyline. Instead it uses suggestion to allow readers the space for their own interpretations and emotions. The feeling of longing in the poem is conveyed subtly, and it is enough.

late autumn
his callused hands
feed the line

Grace Futral
The Paideia School, Age 14, Grade 8, Atlanta, GA

autumn wind
the spool feeding
the thread

Olivia Babuka Black
The Paideia School, Age 15, Grade 9, Atlanta, GA

These poems, both of which we found to be well written, provide together an opportunity to illustrate how similar material can produce very different effects, even in so small a poem as a haiku. Both poems begin by invoking the chill of autumn. Both then present an image of some kind of line being fed out from its source. But the tones of each poem are very different.

The first poem focuses on the hands that are engaged in this task. As such, it suggests a teaching moment, in which the knowledge and skill of one generation is being offered to its successor.

The second poem shows us only the mechanism. Though human hands must surely have been involved in the process at some point, what we are looking at now is part of a machine.

In the first poem, the poet is witnessing not only an activity the older man has been doing for many years, but one that the residents of the place have been doing for hundreds—or even thousands—of years before him. In this way, it is both of the moment and eternal. And the implied outdoor landscape sets this basic human activity in a large physical spaciousness.

In contrast, the sound of the wind outside in the second poem draws the attention indoors to the whirring of a sewing machine. Autumn is a time of turning inward—to indoor activity and introspection. What creative projects will come from those rich, inner processes that happen so readily during the winding-down time of year? In addition, the juxtaposition of the kigo "autumn wind" and the image of the spool feeding the thread bring to mind the passing of time, giving the poem a kind of lonely beauty.

With very similar images, we have poems of community and of solitary reflection, of spaciousness and of the inner world, of the eternal in the ordinary and of impermanence.

This walking-carefully-on-a-crack brings to mind the children's rhyme "step on a crack, break your mother's back." That this poet is deliberately walking on a crack suggests that he or she is probably not superstitious. A person on a tightrope sets one foot in front of the other, gingerly, with arms extended out to each side. In this "tightrope" walk, however, there is no height involved, so any damage resulting from a misstep would be minimal. But so often we feel the need to step carefully and keep balance. Adults and some young people can be so concerned about how they might look to others that they never allow themselves the pure fun of such a moment. A true poet is neither a child nor an adult but rather a creature of and in the moment.

a crack
in the parking lot
I tightrope to the car

Liana Klin
The Paideia School, Age 13, Grade 7, Atlanta, GA

words
come slow like honey
Ohio rain

Coral Lee
Sage Hill School, Age 17, Grade 12,
Newport Coast, CA

While haiku writers avoid using simile, we felt the merits of this poem outweighed that convention. This poem gives the strong sense of place so common in traditional Japanese poetry. In this poem, it comes from more than the poet's just naming the state. Through the repeated vowel sounds in "slow" and "Ohio" and in "come" and "honey," the poet conveys the dreamlike effect of a slow, all-day rain.

As poet John Ciardi pointed out, asking what a poem means may not be as useful a question as asking "how" it means. This haiku is a good example. While one could construct a narrative to account for the images—something about rainy days spent with laconic but eloquent companions—this is not necessary in order to appreciate the poem. The musicality is intense and needs no more explanation than the opening notes of Gershwin's "Rhapsody in Blue."

About our 2013 judges

Mary Stevens lives in the Hudson Valley among much wildlife. A member of Haiku Society of America since 2002, she aspires to get out of her own way when writing haiku. Her haiku have been published in several journals, the 2009 Red Moon Anthology, and the 2005 Snapshot Press Haiku Calendar. She holds an M.S. in Secondary Education, an M.A. in English, and is a lecturer at SUNY New Paltz.

John Stevenson is a former president of the Haiku Society of America, a former editor of *Frogpond,* founding member of the Route 9 Haiku Group *(Upstate Dim Sum)* and current managing editor of *The Heron's Nest.*

The judges for the 2012 competition were Geoffrey Van Kirk and Patricia Doyle Van Kirk.

Haiku written by secondary school students often exhibit some divergent qualities. The poems can soothe, or they may startle. They can strike out in fresh directions, or they may tread familiar paths. They can be in tune with nature or seem wholly absorbed in self. Sometimes they are subtle; sometimes they are really in your face. That is to say, the poems are a good deal like the poets who pen them.

The 457 poems presented to the judges this year in the Nicholas Virgilio Memorial Contest featured this great divergence in topic, treatment, and tone. We took real pleasure in reading them and thank all the poets for their efforts and involvement. Quite a few poems zoomed in on homely topics; many depicted scenes shared with just a single parent or presented the things left behind by a grandparent. The potency of such felt moments of absence was often quite clear, the more so when emotions were evoked in true haiku style rather than expressed or explained. Still, a number of poems lacked the restraint needed in this area. Some student poets chose to tell rather than show, thereby limiting the readers' ability to enter into the poem and explore the feelings inherent in the moment.

After reading the entries on our own, we compared our choices and found there were nearly two dozen poems that made the first cut. Quite a few of these were joint favorites. We conferred; we sifted. In the end a half dozen poems had the spark and the allure to earn our votes as winners for this year's contest. We congratulate these six winners and offer our individual comments on each poem.

~ *Geoff Van Kirk and Patricia Doyle Van Kirk*

This short poem summons us to look and to listen. The images are both delicate and stark. In the winter, that in-between moment, when last light ebbs, can have an elusive beauty. But here, even if the traceries of bare branch against sky seem feathery and pure, the majority of the poem summons a whoosh of sound which suppresses the visual delicacy of nightfall. The whirl of wind is thick enough that crows can congeal it into masses of black and noise.

winter dusk
the crows
clotting the wind

Olivia Babuka Black
The Paideia School, Age 14, Grade 8, Atlanta, GA

Not even mentioned in the poem, but still loud in our ears, is the racket the birds make as they caw and circle. The poet's choice of the word "clotting" here is powerful. It is a wonderful alliterative fit with "crows," and the open vowels of the two words together also suggest, as you say them aloud, the round clumps that are forming in air. However, the use of the verb in the poem also perplexes. Is wind "thick" enough to clot? Is the verb too figurative or metaphoric? While we can pause to explore the image and urge it to make sense, it ultimately succeeds and swirls us along in its wake, tingling with ominous power in the coming darkness. ~gvk

There is a wonderful tangle of natural imagery here, the merging of "winter dusk," "crows," and the "wind." Where the seasonal reference conjures up images of the stillness of the impending darkness, the appearance of the birds, and not just any birds, but luminous, black crows, breaks the scene and the silence. And because these creatures of the air are so agile and perhaps so numerous, they seem to have power over the very wind itself, "clotting" it with their numbers and their flight. The combination is unusual and magical. ~pdvk

at the funeral
headphones hidden
beneath my sweater

Dino Romeo
*Sage High School, Age 14, Grade 9,
Newport Coast, CA*

The author here has a secret. At a time of life when families tend to band together and share communal pain, the poet may be about to tune out. It is easy to leap to the conclusion that, by the very mention of headphones, the speaker is not engaged at this solemn event. Although it's possible the headphones represent a callous wish to be elsewhere, there are other possibilities. This could be a poem about discretion; what's hidden under the sweater may stay hidden out of respect for the moment. Or there may be music cued up which connected the poet and the departed, and, by donning the headphones, our poet would escape into rather than escape from the moment. In any case, there's an appealing honesty to the poet's revelation of what's hiding behind the sweater. The haiku invites us to explore the ways, as individuals and as families, we approach what's momentous in life. ~gvk

This poem offers a wonderful juxtaposition,
pairing the image of a "funeral" and all the
associations it conjures up for the reader with the
subsequent, unexpected image of the "hidden" music
"headphones." So we imagine the narrator present,
not just at a funeral, but at "the" funeral, which
implies it is for someone special or important. And
in the midst of what is generally a solemn, dignified,
even ancient, ritual, modern technology intrudes. Is
music being played secretly as a distraction? Does it
provide some comfort? Is the speaker only here out of
obligation and, dare I say it, perhaps a little bored?
Or have the headphones been left on inadvertently?
Is there music even playing? ~pdvk

Those summer waves—they're powerful. Ride one
wrong and, thunk, it tumbles you to the bottom. You
come up sputtering, anointed with salt and sand.
And then you do it again! In this poem, the waves
reemerge powerful, almost personified. They reappear
at home and seem to laugh as the poet does a last
scrub. The remnants from a day at the shore, they
cling! In the poem the beach sand goes toward the
drain. But what about the sunburn? What about
the echoes of waves crashing toward the beach and
the sibilant rush they make sliding back the sandy
slopes? It's all still with us long after the sun has
set. Through a homely, amusing image, this haiku
immerses us in the whole magic of a seaside day.
~gvk

I like the way this poem captures an experience
most of us have had, coming inside after a day at the
beach, sun-soaked and water-logged, mellow and
contented, but wanting to hit the showers first thing
to wash off all that pesky sand. Sea sand, while fun
to walk and play in on the beach, feels all the more
uncomfortable the further we get from the shore. This
writer offers us a playful take on this common scene
with the use of the alliterative image of "belly button
sand," which is reminiscent of childhood, and also
manages to link the recent past of the beach visit to

summer waves
leave belly button sand
in my shower

Alex Manolakas
Sage High School, Age18, Grade 12,
Newport Coast, CA

the sandy aftermath with the "summer waves" that "leave" the sand in the "shower." Outdoors effectively merges with indoors. The choice of the proprietary word "my," rather than "the," with "shower" is also intriguing, implying that the trip back from the beach is a return to the comforts of home, or at least to a familiar spot. ~pdvk

This simple poem speaks of the drab and damp. As each line progresses, the poem widens a bit until the last line spreads out in imitation of the puddles it describes. But the poem is not just a portrait in monochrome. It seems to be about perception as much as it is about precipitation. While many of us bow in response to falling rain, the grammar of the poem says that puddles are the canvas, but the leaden sky is the subject and story of the last two lines. It's a bit of an inversion, isn't it, looking down to see what's up? The sky, be it boiling grey masses or flannel blankets, is at our feet. And if the puddles cover pale concrete, will the heavens look the same as when the puddles blanket playground asphalt? Does a falling drop spread rings? It's an imperfect view, this reflected vision of sky, and certainly an impermanent one. But who's to say we'd get closer to the truth of clouds by looking up? The poem here acknowledges that we may sometimes come to know a thing by its reflection and by what it brings to pass. ~gvk

rainfall
grey sky
in big puddles

Siani Macklin
Sacred Heart School, Age 13,
Grade 7, Camden, NJ

This haiku poem caught my attention immediately and left me pondering what "grey sky" in "big puddles" really looks like. As a long-time puddle splasher myself (the bigger the puddle, the better, by the way), I realized I couldn't quite imagine it, probably because any opportunity to view the reflection of the sky was lost with all that splashing. The writer reminded me that stopping to observe the beauty of this natural phenomenon was as important as playing in it. And the scaffolding of three lines, starting with one word, moving to two, and then three, knits the three different but connected images of the haiku delicately together for the reader. ~pdvk

Here, in simple words, the poet presents a scene of quietness and delicacy. The two sections of the poem are well set out and sonically distinct. The hard consonant sounds of both "night" and "lake" make for a definitive beginning. In the hush of a still night by the water, all sounds are amplified. If you were in a canoe, a light bump of paddle on hull would resound the way the "k" sound clobbers the long "a" in the word lake. But the poet, alert and alive, hears no jarring sound. Instead, the last two lines present a mystical moment. In touching the moon, perhaps with finger or paddle brought to still water, the poet takes advantage of the quiet to make this delicate connection. The long, open vowels help to stretch out the phrase and highlight the moment of intimacy.
~gvk

night on the lake
I touch
the moon

Abbey Shannon
The Paideia School, Age 13,
Grade 7, Atlanta, GA

At first this poem appears to describe a fairly normal sight in nature, the moon's reflection in water. A closer look shows there is actually a lot more going on here. Is the speaker reaching down to graze the lake water with a gentle hand to "touch" the reflected "moon"? Or is this about standing on tiptoes and stretching towards the unreachable sky? Or is this, in fact, suggesting a figurative image about someone having achieved something great by soaring to the moon's heights? Or trying to? And what brought the speaker here? Is the speaker alone? Or with others? I wonder. In just eight words, this appealing haiku presents a scene open to many possible interpretations.
~pdvk

While this haiku, with its short second line, has sort of stuttering line breaks, that staccato writing works in its favor. This is because the poet has depicted a story that is equally full of jarring motion. In addition, the succession of clipped consonants in all three lines gives a wonderful sonic echo to the painful progress of footsteps along this root-bound path. Is the poet going up or down? Each way would have its own challenges. What seems more important is the poet's own determination to take the roughest route. By tramping on each knot, the poet hits the hard spots. Even if the

stair of roots
I step
on each knot

Ainura Johnson
The Paideia School, Age 13,
Grade 7, Atlanta, GA

goal is to get the maximum traction on what could be slippery terrain, the poet has committed to the more difficult path. Sometimes there's no better choice. ~gvk

This haiku, aptly reflective of its meaning, seems to be structured very much like the actual steps of a staircase, with one three-word, three-syllable step on top of another, separated by a smaller, two-word, two-syllable riser. Beyond that, it works on many levels. The roots may have sprawled across a staircase in the park, or they may have formed a natural one over time. The inclusion of the human "I" in the scene reminds us that nature was there first and may sometimes impede human progress, in this case, up or down a staircase, or it may do the exact opposite, providing a means to assist us on our journey. It's all part of the natural order. Interestingly, the speaker here seems up for the challenge of overcoming any obstacles, in fact, almost going out of the way to "step on each knot" in the series of roots. Perhaps it is an inviting challenge. This haiku is certainly inviting. ~pdvk

About our 2012 judges

Geoffrey Van Kirk, a teacher, photographer, haiku poet and haiku workshop leader, has taught English to middle school students at the United Nations International School for 20 years. He is one of the two organizers of the Student Haiku Contest, an annual poetry competition sponsored by UNIS for students writing haiku in Japanese and/or English. He has published haiku in a number of journals.

Patricia Doyle Van Kirk is a teacher at the United Nations International School and has served as Head of the English Department there for well over two decades. A Senior Examiner for the International Baccalaureate program and IB workshop leader, she teaches middle school and high school, and both she and her students have won prizes in haiku poetry competitions.

The judges for the 2011 competition were Francine Banwarth and Tom Painting.

November is the eleventh month of the year; the word itself suggests a feeling of longing as our eyes are directed toward the wide expanse of sky. Each line is balanced with four well-chosen syllables and a controlled rhythm that moves the reader through the poem. One can only wonder at the origin of the seed. Is it from a meadow, a vacant city lot? The November sky foreshadows winter, the imagery of which often centers on grief, distance, loss, and at times serenity. There is a vulnerability suggested in this haiku, but also a hint of hope. Will this seed come to rest on fertile ground? Will it fulfill its promise? The poet has fulfilled hers/his in this well-crafted haiku which gives us something to ponder.

November sky
a lone seed drifts
on wispy wings

Martine Thomas
*Wilson Commencement School,
Age 14, Grade 9, Rochester, NY*

This haiku engages our senses—sight, sound, smell, touch, perhaps even taste. "Eau de rain" is in and of itself a lovely expression. In translation from the French, "eau de" may be interpreted as "scent of." The use of the French language adds a hint of mystery: nature's perfume, or the scent of some human presence? Together with the opening line and the well-chosen verb "drifts" in line three, the poem flirts with the notion of change, a shift in the weather and for that matter the season that can be perceived through the senses.

August night
eau de rain
drifts on the wind

Martine Thomas
*Wilson Commencement School,
Age 14, Grade 9, Rochester, NY*

AP Physics
my eyes
twitch

Heather Zadra
Sage Hill School, Age 18,
Grade 12, Newport Coast, CA

One measure of a successful senryu is to elicit from the reader a near instantaneous response. With a delightful and effective use of juxtaposition, there is no need to guess what this young author experiences as the brain tries to navigate advanced study in physics. If physics is the study of matter and its motion through space-time, then the poet has taken a moment along the continuum and made a precise and valid observation, the meaning of which registered with us at the speed of light.

story time
under the covers
the night's warm whispers

Mariah Wilson
Sage Hill School, Age 14,
Grade 9, Newport Coast, CA

The alliterative quality of the words chosen by the poet is admired in this senryu. Upon reflection, Tom found himself remembering the bedtime stories told to him as a child and in more recent times having the pleasure of telling some of those same stories to his own children. The ritual of story time is timeless. The middle line of this poem serves as a pivot. It works simultaneously with the first and third lines and evokes a feeling of seamlessness. The poet is aware of the special relationship between the storyteller and listener, a quiet moment of warm intimacy as the noise of the day fades away to sleep and dreams.

About our 2011 judges

Francine Banwarth began writing and studying haiku in 1988. She is a co-founder of Haiku Dubuque and leads haiku workshops at The Foundry Books in Mineral Point, Wisconsin. She served as second vice president of the Haiku Society of America for three years and currently serves on the board of *Modern Haiku*. Her work appears in a variety of journals, anthologies, and contests. She is refining a workshop, "A Writing Life in Seventeen Syllables or Less," presented at the May 2011 Haiku Society of America Midwest regional meeting in Evanston, IL.

Tom Painting taught middle and high school creative writing for 17 years at School of the Arts in Rochester, NY. He has been active in the haiku community for more than a decade. He served as first and second vice-president of the Haiku Society of America and was co-editor the editor of the 2005 Haiku Society of America member's anthology. Most recently Tom taught a haiku course for adults at The Institute for Lifelong Learning at Emory University in Atlanta where he now resides.

2010

The judges for the 2010 competition were Janelle Barrera and Fran Masat.

Presented with 1,575 student haiku, we decided to read all on our own and then compare notes. In our top twenty picks, we each chose two of the same haiku. That was a real start! From there, our next top 20 produced the remaining four winners. While there is no particular order in the list of winners, the first two listed are the first two haiku we chose.

The students wrote about insightful moments related to nature, friends, family, and pets. Human nature took precedence over nature, per se, yet it is always there setting the scene. These are our top six choices, but there were many more in close contention. Thanks to each of the young authors.

~ Janelle Barrera and Fran Masat

autumn rain
rinsing the color
from the leaves

Lauren Winters
Hilliard Davidson High School,
Age 18, Grade 12, Hilliard, OH

That a storm has downed leaves is not unusual. But here, in a refreshing manner, the author notes the more sensitive loss, that of color. More broadly, the haiku illustrates the notion of age diminishing the quality of life and that resonates with all of us.

cold night
the phone call…
from a disowned sister

Hanna Amireh
School of the Arts, Age 17,
Grade 12, Rochester, NY

We've all waited for a phone call. As cold night sets the tone and scene, the pivotal second line provides an almost proverbial structure: "the phone call…" That the call is from a disowned sister sheds light on an almost universal vulnerability—on both ends of the phone. What happens next will reveal much about ourselves and how we relate to such events.

on the windowsill
next to the box of ashes
Jiro's dog collar

Michelle Hosoda
Sage Hill School, Age 17,
Grade 12, Newport Coast, CA

A first impression may be that of a memorial to companionship, but there is more. The ashes are not identified, though "next to" does hint at the link between them and Jiro. Instead, it is the empty circle of the collar that evokes a desire to look beyond the sill and glimpse what that linkage may represent.

rural Peru
5 lollypops
for a handmade bracelet

Caitlin Sullivan
Sage Hill School, Age 18,
Grade 12, Newport Coast, CA

"5 lollypops" seems out of place in rural Peru until we re-think the trade proposed. The contrasts of machined candy to rural handicraft and of dissolving sweetness to tangible artifact provide deeper insight into the nature of the scene. By comparing the differing wants of two cultures, the haiku thus provides a resonant view of our global society.

Grandad's funeral
she wonders
whether she looks fat

Alice Liu
Sage Hill School, Age 14,
Grade 9, Newport Coast, CA

At most gatherings, there always seems to be someone who, obviously, is wondering about themselves. Maybe the thought is real, or perhaps it's unconscious self-protection from the truths of the gathering, in this case death. We are held until the last word before we are given a clue as to which. Even then, it is our interpretation—but isn't it always?

under the shade
of sunflowers,
my mouse decays

Laura Hansen
Capital High School, Age 18,
Grade 12, Boise, ID

So many things can happen in the shade of sunflowers. Here, in a straightforward and void of melancholy manner, it is the slow sureness of decay that illuminates that shade. In a broader and almost celebratory sense, life rises above death.

About our 2010 judges

Janelle Barrera is a former teacher and now tutors foreign language students in Key West. She enjoys writing haiku with school children and has published haiku, haibun and poetry. She and Francis Masat are co-editors of the "Key Ku" column in *Solares Hill*, a weekly Sunday magazine, and she was instrumental in introducing haiku workshops to the annual Robert Frost Poetry Festival in Key West. "Reading the students' haiku was a genuine pleasure," she says.

Francis Masat lives in Key West, FL. With over 1000 poems and haiku in over 100 journals, his recent chapbooks are *Lilacs After Winter* (haibun), MET Press, *A Taste of Key West,* Pudding House Press, and *Threshing,* March Street Press.

The judges for the 2009 competition were Kristen Deming and Bill Kenney.

As the judges in this year's Nicholas A. Virgilio Memorial Haiku Competition, we set out hoping that we would find a new and fresh perspective, the "voice of youth," from the young poets who participated. We have not been disappointed. We have taken a look at the future of haiku, and it is working. The judges were struck by the variety, the sharpness of observation, the richness of imagination, and the formal discipline that characterized much of what we were privileged to read. We are pained but pleased when we reflect on the quality of many of the poems that did not make the final cut.

Where our young poets stumbled, it was often out of a failure to trust in their own experience and perceptions. A forced effort at the dramatic, often edging over into the melodramatic, was a common problem. And the principle of juxtaposition central to the haiku form was not grasped with equal clarity by all contestants: some merely spread a sentiment over three lines, and a few simply offered a list of three fragments.

But, above all, the poets and their work exemplified an energy and vitality that can only portend well for the form we love. Some of thesm, we are sure, will be heard from again.

It was a pleasure and a privilege to serve as your judges this year. Our thanks go to the sponsors of the contest and to the teachers who supported and encouraged the participants. We acknowledge and commend the energy, the spirit, and the promise of all the contestants. And we congratulate the authors of the prize-winning poems.

~ *Kristen Deming and Bill Kenney*

In this haiku, the long vowel sounds help to create a feeling of calm, bringing us directly within the sensory experience of the poet. Looking through a window at the gazebo, we see it dressed as though it were some kind of theatrical set. The fresh snow has transformed the landscape, blending everything into an elegant harmony of white shapes against the darkness. In the absence of wind on this quiet night, the snow lies undisturbed. It is as though the scene exists entirely for our visual pleasure. It is the quiet itself that has been made visible.

quiet night
the gazebo
dressed with snow

Meredith Jeffers
School of the Arts, Age 16,
Grade 10, Rochester, NY

**winter night
cracks in the floorboards
widen**

Mary Rice
*School of the Arts, Age 16,
Grade 10, Rochester, NY*

In this spare and objective poem, the poet invites the reader to explore, through imagination and memory, a range of possible meanings. Is the poet alone on this winter night? Surely there is nothing like a winter night to create a sense of isolation. The winter season brings snow and ice, but it also makes itself felt in subtle, often unnoticed ways. The poet detects the presence of winter in a place we do not expect to find it: inside the home, where we feel enclosed and protected from what is happening outside. But even here, beneath our feet, the floorboards are expanding and contracting minutely within the larger flow of seasons. Standing alone in the last line, "widen" suggests an unwanted opening through which, we imagine, anything might enter. How weak, when all is said and done, are our defenses against the elements.

**saying goodbye
the river flowing
one way**

Cindy Truong
*School of the Arts, Age 13,
Grade 8, Rochester, NY*

The young poet clearly understands that in haiku the juxtaposition and interaction of images suggest more than is directly stated. Here the passing human moment is contrasted to ongoing nature. Saying goodbye, the poet is at the same time aware of the river's powerful current. We do not know if the parting is temporary or final. Especially when we are young, but not only then, we like to believe that no goodbye is truly final. But our poet has perceived in nature a hint of the irreversible: the "one way" flow that unites the natural movement and the human moment. How many times can we step into the same river?

**tornado drill
the hallways full
of laughter**

Nikki Savary
*Wahlert High School, Age 18,
Grade 12, Dubuque, IA*

The two parts of the poem form an unlikely combination. A tornado is not a laughing matter, but for young people escaping class for a short time in a large group of their peers, such a disaster may seem unimaginable. The drill has become a social event. A tornado is a force of nature, but so is a hallway full of kids. And what kids have ever taken a tornado drill, or fire drill, or any kind of drill, as seriously as they should, or, anyway, as seriously as the grown-ups think they should? In this poem, we see the carefree, unbounded optimism of young people. And the elegant pivot around the single word "full" exhibits a formal control of which many an established haijin could be proud.

You have to like the boldness, quirkiness, and impishness of this young poet's imagination. In lines 2-3 we find an extravagance that could easily trip up an experienced poet. But it works here because nature has its own extravagances, and they include the extremes of winter in a cold climate. A beard frozen in place? Not every day, but not unheard of, either, and that's the sort of winter this poet is talking about. Moreover, these lines serve a further function as an imagistic definition of line 1: Haven't we always suspected that this is what Old Man Winter looks like?

winter
the old man's beard
frozen in place

Riley Siwiec
*School of the Arts, Age 12,
Grade 7, Rochester, NY*

How many haiku have gazed at footprints in the snow? Here the poet has discovered, and put into practice, an important principle of haiku: that clarity, simplicity, and freshness of vision can make most things new. The first line points us forward, in the direction of the unbroken snow, setting up the look back over the shoulder that is the business of the next two lines. The near naivete of expression in these lines suggests a moment of pure, delighted awareness. We recognize the voice of the playful, childlike spirit, pleased in this moment to leave its mark. That we always leave a trail is a truth that may not be quite so gleefully accepted, however, as the poet grows older.

new snow
my footprints
follow me

Martine Thomas
*School of the Arts, Age 12,
Grade 7, Rochester, NY*

2008

The judges for the 2008 competition were Tony Pupello and Pamela Miller Ness.

We would like to express our appreciation to all the young poets who submitted to this year's contest and to the teachers who instructed them in the craft and special characteristics of haiku. It was a privilege to be invited to enter their haiku moments and a pleasure to share their imagery and language. Each of us first read and re-read the submissions numerous times; we then met to discuss our preliminary selections and to undertake the challenging task of selecting six poems (unranked) that we consider most exemplary of fine haiku. And it was a challenging task. Many of the entries were sophisticated in their use of imagery and juxtaposition and were very proficiently crafted. As with very fine haiku and senryu, many were layered and functioned on multiple levels.

Of course, while any finalist must exhibit many of the salient characteristics of haiku, we also looked for poems that surprised or delighted us and expanded our experience through imagery, language, and/or emotional resonance. As R. H. Blyth wrote, "A haiku is the expression of a temporary enlightenment, in which we see into the life of things" (Haiku, volume 1).

~ Tony Pupello and Pamela Miller Ness

The poet subtly creates multiple layers of juxtaposition: interior and exterior; the white of snow, stars, and walls; and a single human being within the vast universe. S/he captures essential elements of classical Japanese haiku, yugen (mystery) and sabi (essential aloneness) and leaves the reader with an unfinished narrative. It is the reader's job to enter into this powerful and mysterious haiku to complete the story.

winter stars
my father paints over
the old white walls

Asha Bishi
School of the Arts, Age 18,
12th Grade, Rochester, NY

autumn night
one brick
darker than the rest

Gracie Elliot
School of the Arts, Age 12,
7th Grade, Rochester NY

This poet also sets the scene with a kigo, autumn night, suggesting the various connotations of autumn; a time of change, shorter days, and the onset of cold weather. S/he effectively juxtaposes the vastness of a night sky with a single human-made brick and the darkness of the night with one dark brick. The combined imagery of the night sky and the fact that all the bricks are dark give this poem a deeply melancholy mood. There is no light except for the illumination of the poet's keen observation and beautifully crafted language, the crispness of the night so carefully reflected in the repetition of t's and k's.

first kiss —
the tingle of coke
down her throat

Lauren Fresch
Perkins High School, Age 17,
Grade 12, Sandusky, OH

This is an excellent example of a contemporary senryu: ingenuous, humorous, and at the same time deeply moving. How perfectly the poet captures first love through such specific sensory imagery, a kiss shared over a coke, both of which tingle in her throat. This poet should also be commended for his/her carefully crafted language: the alliteration of kiss and coke, the onomatopoeic use of kiss and tingle, and the assonance of coke and throat.

scent of spring
my sister paints
the rising sun

Asha Bishi
School of the Arts, Age 18,
Grade 12, Rochester, NY

This is an excellent example of how what might be a trite kigo expression, "scent of spring," is used as the springboard to a delightful, lovely and spare moment. A moment of fragrant breezes combined with the lightness and brightness of the rising sun—a moment that may be overdone—is turned into a real moment of spring bursting forth found in the act of "sister painting." This poem turns on the unselfishness of the author—sharing this moment of creation with her/his sister and sharing sister's creation with us. And this glorious moment of rebirth and renewal is presented in very simple, understated terms.

A deeply evocative poem, this piece resonates in the absence of sound. A "silent graveyard" is a commonplace and perhaps overdone image. After all, what is a graveyard if not silent, if not the absence of sound and the activity of life? Yet oft-times we, the living, disturb the graveyard's silence with our own intrusions. Perhaps uncomfortable we chatter, we joke, we stir. In this piece the poet has succeeded in capturing and reinforcing the disturbing silences. The normally rambunctious and extremely loud crow sits silently in stillness atop a tombstone—forcing us, the readers, to put aside all and become part of that most uncomfortable silence.

silent graveyard
one tombstone
with a crow

Alexa Navarez
*School of the Arts, Age 12,
Grade 7, Rochester, NY*

The lightness of the snow, and the heaviness of alcoholism. These are two elements the poet deftly weaves together for us in this finely crafted poem. At first, we are confronted with an air of untruth, anathema in haiku. How could anyone who's drunk step lightly? Drunks are heavy, have uncontrollably heavy movements, and are not graceful in the least. Aren't they? Once again, the reader is called, pulled, into the narrative. This is not an attempt at a desktop haiku, an image written because it fits right in the author's imagination. This is a sad piece about an all-too-common disease. The author is painfully aware of how graceful, how light an alcoholic can appear on the surface. Yes, the drunk passes over almost unnoticed, certainly his light footsteps do not give him away – but his breath does.

light footsteps
across the snow
his alcohol breath

Desire Giddens
*School of the Arts, Age 12,
Grade 7, Rochester, NY*

The judges for the 2007 competition were Ruth Eshbaugh and Susan Delaney.

Haiku and senryu in their brevity are an art to master. Most of the entries to the Nicholas A. Virgilio Haiku Contest this year were senryu. Some missed the form of haiku or senryu altogether. Still in the entries we found again and again powerful images that showed thought and vulnerability. All the submissions gave us a delightful and interesting look into the young author's world. The scope of content ranging from the mundane to the highly unusual thus showed an attempt by the authors to look at their world fresh with eyes open, senses at alert.

~ *Ruth Eshbaugh and Susan Delaney*

There is a heart wrenching story behind this senryu, with life so precariously hanging in the balance that the author falters between despair and hope. With each heartbeat life continues. As long as there is a heartbeat there is hope. There is sense of waiting beside a bedside, held captive by the monitor, distanced by technology, but informed by it also. It is a surreal moment that anyone who has sat in that chair can slip into in a heartbeat upon reading the senryu.

beep of the monitor
reminding me…
to hope

Nicole Grogan
Wahlert High School, Grade 12, Dubuque, IA

Expectation good or bad, anticipation of an encounter or the dread of a long lonely day is the stuff that Valentine's Day is made of. The color red like a stop light can't be ignored. Even if you want the day to end or want it to last forever the feeling of stress can't be ignored. It is the annoyance of a long red light when you are waiting for something more in life to happen but instead you are sitting in your car at a red light waiting.

Valentine's Day
the stop light stays red
too long

Pendle Marshall-Hallmark
School of the Arts, Grade 9, Rochester, NY

The wind brings mystery into this simple senryu of two young girls sharing a secret. The very economical use of words suggests briefness. The secret is shared, the words spoken and are gone as quickly and silently and mysteriously as the wind. A secret shared is not to be repeated thus exists but does not exist except between those who share it. An excellent expression in nature of the relationship is implied in this work. The word "taking" suggests something stolen or forbidden to share.

This senryu could also be read as someone with no one to share a secret. They speak instead into the wind, creating a profound sense of aloneness and alienation by one who holds a secret that no human ear can hear.

the wind
taking
her secret

Jordan Krueger
*Wahlert High School, Grade 12,
Dubuque, IA*

You can feel the cold crisp air and the sense of determination in each step. A young girl with her life ahead of her like the new spring day is full of promise. The comparison to a willow speaks of fluidity of movement and grace; a profound enjoyable evocative image of "youth." The rhythm of her step around a circular path is repeated in the mention of the season with its own circular rhythm.

early spring
the willowy girl
runs around the track

Sara Dill
*School of the Arts, Grade 8,
Rochester, NY*

Jelly shoes stand out as a delightfully unusual but recognizable image. It evokes an array of colors, although in this haiku the color is unnamed. The smooth texture of the shoe and the suggestion of wetness or even a puddle by the use of the word "dry" repeats the smooth surface and shape of the shoes. They are empty on the porch, but someone has worn them. They suggest a story, but it is left unsaid. So much is unsaid in this timeless glimpse of the mundane invaded by the colorful shoe that it makes a very interesting senryu to ponder.

spring morning
her jelly shoes dry
on the back porch

Zoe Christopher
*School of the Arts, Grade 9,
Rochester, NY*

A mood is created in this senryu with many echoes or layers. There is the sight of the empty house, the mood that emptiness creates. The smell of the rotting wood is another layer that tells us the house is old and abandoned for years. The echoes of laughter are in the present and past connecting the unauthorized visitors that explore the empty rooms with the strangers who lived there at one time. Why do we love to explore abandoned places?

empty house
echoes of laughter
in the rotting wood

Emily Onyan
*School of the Arts, Grade 8,
Rochester, NY*

The judges for the 2006 competition were Michael Ketchek and Jerome Cushman.

Judging this contest was a pleasure. There were nearly 30 excellent poems that fit the definitions of haiku or senryu and could have placed in the top six. There were many excellent poets, who we hope will continue to create. We encourage them to send their best poems to the many haiku journals and magazines in print and on the Internet. Many of the poems we read should be seen by the haiku world.

However, there were several poems that lacked the form and feeling of haiku or senryu. We wish that the teachers who encouraged these students to enter this contest were more aware of the structure and style of contemporary haiku. This can be learned by reading haiku in the well-known periodicals and many sites on the Web. Teachers and students can also encourage their libraries to purchase some of the fine haiku books that are available, such as *The Haiku Handbook,* by William J. Higginson and Penny Harter, *Haiku: A Poet's Guide,* by Lee Gurga, or *Writing and Enjoying Haiku,* by Jane Reichhold. These will help everyone achieve a better grasp of the elements of successful haiku and senryu.

~ *Michael Ketchek and Jerome Cushman*

Forget about politics and think about the image of urine hitting hot sand, being soaked up by the earth, and soon disappearing. This image aloe can bring about many thoughts concerning the relationship between man and nature. Certainly, the insignificance of one man in comparison to the vast desert is highlighted by how little effect one man's water has on all that dryness. A man in the desert is a lonely image. Add to that the loneliness of a soldier in a foreign land to get a feeling for all that is implied by this haiku. Now and only now add the political implications and this haiku has even more layers of meaning. It nicely demonstrates how to blend contemporary and eternal issues into a successful poem.

Iraqi sun
an American soldier
pisses in the sand

Elishma Farquharson
School of the Arts, Age 18,
Grade 12, Rochester, NY

three stones on a fence

Cory Steinmetz
Vermilion High School, Age 17,
Grade 11, Vermilion, OH

new year's day
walking in yesterday's
frozen footprints

Allen Bartter
School of the Arts, Age 17,
Grade 11, Rochester, NY

fireworks
a boy nestles
into his mother

Fantazia Edic
School of the Arts, Age 18,
Grade 12, Rochester, NY

Don't let the simplicity of this short one line haiku fool you. In it is the mystery of human creativity. The poet has created a scene in which we are told very little, but are given a huge amount to contemplate. There are three stones on a fence that had to have been placed there on purpose. One or two stones could be perceived as mindless human action but three is enough to indicate a plan. Thankfully we are not given a clue as to the nature of this plan. These three stones remain a small mysterious Stonehenge. And as in Stonehenge, contemplating the mystery is endlessly engaging.

This haiku, with its clean, clear imagery, speaks of the relationship of the present and the future to the past. For all the talk of new beginnings on New Year's Day, the past remains unchanging and influential. In a poetic and personal way this haiku says something very similar to what Karl Marx wrote, "Men make their own history, but they do not make it just as they please; they do not make it under circumstances chosen by themselves, but under circumstances directly encountered, given, and transmitted from the past." They make it, "walking in yesterday's frozen footprints."

Vivid images universal and at the same time very personal, come to mind with this plain and poignant haiku. The vastness of the whole sky filled with bright colors and loud sounds is quickly refocused to a child seeking the security and warmth of his mother. Time, place, and characters we care about, all in an emotional event, are clearly drawn here.

Seven words and eleven syllables paint a mural for both the young and us old guys. The interesting use of the sibilant "s" in each line also helps us recall the sound of those rockets shooting into the sky. Even after reading this poem many times we come back to it for yet more images.

Here is a clever use of synesthesia, drawing the tactile and auditory senses into one experience. The feeling of that "coarse wool" and the sound of the cricket outside blend into a unique, melancholy moment. The use of "rasp" for the cricket's sound in late autumn is appropriate for the intended metaphor.

This verbless haiku presents us with a sensation-packed event that can be shared by many readers. Here, too, the sounds of the words reinforce the images. The poet uses just eleven syllables and nine words to produce a powerful poem.

the coarse wool
of my blanket
a cricket's rasp

Giulia Perucchio
School of the Arts, Age 15, Grade 10, Rochester, NY

This is a special poem by and for the adolescent. That image of the "bean stalks" brings to mind the concept of something fast growing and also the children's tale Jack and the Beanstalk. The second line jars the mind, taking it in a very different direction. Here is another poem that uses clever juxtaposition of images that present us with two independent ideas synthesized into a wonderful story.

The growth spurts that make a youth feel out of clothes, out of sorts, and out of place are common to many teenagers. The way "fit" sits there all alone on the third line reflects the awkwardness and loneliness that a fast-growing young person often experiences.

bean stalks
none of my clothes
fit

Gen Poehner
School of the Arts, Age 16, Grade 11, Rochester, NY

The judges for the 2005 competition were Michael Moore and Charles Trumbull.

We noticed a few things about the contest entries. All winning entries are closer to senryu than haiku; that is, they deal more with human nature than with nature. None of the winning haiku used punctuation. The idea of a haiku comprising two images has been nailed home by these student poets. The contest images, in fact, were not infrequently too far apart for comprehension. Many of the entries contain a personal reference, which is normally avoided in haiku. Four of the six winners contain the word "my." Many haiku among the entrants were about haiku, grandmothers, and small children.

Reading the work entered by poets in the Virgilio Haiku Contest was a wonderful experience. Each poet should be proud of their individual contribution to this literary event. For those of you who were not selected as winners, please continue to share your talent as writer of haiku and share your talent with others.

~ Michael Moore and Charles Trumbull

Various views of life, death, and permanence are powerfully placed together in this prizewinning haiku for 2005. The adults gathered at the wake are undoubtedly observing the age-old church traditions for celebrating the end of a life, emphasizing continuities and eternities. The little cousin shows a much more transitory view of creations: one shake and they are gone, ready to be repeated.

A child's hands upon an etch-a-sketch erase and yet draw a picture that captures the finality of death. That moment is recorded in a literary snapshot, of two cousins during their grandmother's wake. The poet fills the scene with the motion of youthful innocence and the motionless nature of death. Yet life for the two cousins' creativity lives on. "Little cousin shakes her etch-a-sketch" and a poet shares a few insightful words.

grandma's wake
my little cousin
shakes her etch-a-sketch

Alex Degus
*School of the Arts, Age 18,
Grade 12, Rochester, NY*

memories
caught in my brush
long strands

Guilia Perucchio
School of the Arts, Age 14,
Grade 9, Rochester, NY

For the writer what may have once been just "my brush" has acquired a special significance because of the "long strands." The question now arises; who does the hair belong to? If it is the hair of the poet, the significance of its length may remind the poet of younger days. If it is not the poet's, one can surmise that the poet has shared the brush with someone whose hair is longer than the poet's. We are left to ponder the question. I love a mystery.

What would be more likely to induce deep personal thought and memories than the repetitive brushing of hair at night. My mind's eye sees a young lady sitting before a mirror in her dressing gown dreamily brushing her hair and almost measuring out her life strand by strand. A wonderful image!

pre-school
a triangle block
stuck in a square hole

Allen Bartter
School of the Arts, Age 15,
Grade 10, Rochester, NY

This haiku is both philosophical and very funny. There is the suggestion that if you want to get something tricky done —"a square peg in a round hole"—perhaps you need to go study the youngsters: bypass the basics and… just jam it in!

Here the reader is given the opportunity to take the poem at face value or rearrange the triangle block in his or her mind. The what is, or what ought to be, that is the question. The word "stuck" may cause the mind to wonder how the triangle was placed in the hole, was it forced or just placed there with ease? Does it matter? A moment in the poet's eye lets us see that design is a state of mind. A triangle stuck in a square hole shows that a young person was exploring another way of looking at how the world works.

harvest moon
the homeless man's cup
filled with silver

Kate Bosek-Sills
School of the Arts, Age 15,
Grade 10, Rochester, NY

In this haiku a celestial event is brought to earth. By looking down the reader sees that which glows from above, reflected in the cup of a homeless man. This haiku gives the reader a number of ideas to reflect upon. From the ethereal nature of light to the earthiness of the homeless man. The multidimensional nature of this haiku makes it a joy to read.

The homeless man's cup is finally full, not of the one kind of silver he wishes for, but something much different. Alas, only if he is a poet will he be able to rejoice much.

classical haiku: using an image from nature to link to and describe a human subject. Because of the two juxtaposed images, the delighted reader receives a crystal-clear portrait of a man at one with his environment.

I can see the golden "stubbled wheat field" with the evening sun hanging heavy in the western sky. The poet gives the reader a wonderful view of a landscape. A landscape touched by rays of the sun and care of his/her father's hand.

my father
in the stubbled wheat field
scratches his beard

Asha Bishi
School of the Arts, Age 14,
Grade 9, Rochester, NY

This author employs a device of

Does a person's superstition last as long as they can remember that their belief system is alive and well playing a role in their life? I would like to think that when the poet opened a fortune cookie that fate had good things in store. The power of suggestion is illustrated in the words of this intriguing dilemma.

Many people look beyond the normal for clues to their fate or the way to conduct their lives. Sealing a fate-especially in a young person-seems excessive, and yet… Do you really think it is mere hyperbole that a young person would be so superstitious as to put all his/her eggs in one basket?

superstitious
a fortune cookie
seals my fate

Adrian DiMatteo
School of the Arts, Age 14,
Grade 9, Rochester, NY

The judges for the 2004 competition were an'ya and kirsty karkow.

It has given us enormous pleasure, and we've felt honored to read so many haiku from so many fine upcoming young poets. For the most part, they are happy, exuberant haiku full of light-hearted energy. There is also a keen sense of place and the feeling that these are true experiences. It may be noted that none of the haiku that we have chosen use capital letters, or even much in the way of punctuation. We have looked for fresh images, juxtaposition, use of all five senses, and haiku that show rather than tell of an event or feeling, leading the reader to think more deeply. To those whose haiku do not appear below, please remember that poetry is subjective, and at another time and place, your haiku might well be the one chosen. Our warmest congratulations to the finalists, and thank you to all those who submitted haiku, for their interest and effort. Bravo!

~ *an'ya and kirsty karkow*

Considering all the varied shapes and shadows on the shore, this seal cannot be seen unless the poet is very quiet, studying the scene as words of a haiku start to form. Imagine the happiness as she/ he suddenly notices a sleeping seal; this feeling of wonder conveyed to the reader. The form of the seal is indeed "lost", camouflaged, and this moment is very nicely rendered in classic haiku form. ~kk

A fine zoom effect in this haiku, from the wide setting of a vast ocean shore being lost in a pile of rocks, to the last line when the writer allows us to see a sleeping seal. Just as if this seal is nestled safely in the rock arms of the sea itself. Multiple images of ocean, shore, rocks, a seal, yet all tied together in a common theme to form a complete haiku moment. ~an'ya

ocean shore
lost in a pile of rocks
a seal sleeps

James Kelly
Wahlert High School, Age 17,
Dubuque, IA

cold in church
mother and I
move closer

Amanda White
Wahlert High School, Age 17,
Dubuque, IA

A successful haiku leads the reader to deeper thoughts with each reading. This one succeeds. The poet and his/her mother move closer not only physically, but possibly spiritually and emotionally as well. There is excellent use of alliteration. ~kk

This haiku has deeper layered meaning than it appears to have at first reading. I feel the coldness perhaps of an old stone church, juxtaposed with the warmth of a mother/daughter or mother/son relationship. This could possibly have deep religious implications as well with the mother image representative of the Virgin Mary, although the author skillfully leaves it up to reader interpretation. ~an'ya

summer cottage
the bullfrog
slips my grasp

Emily Cornish
School of the Arts, Age 15,
Rochester, NY

For me, this haiku tells of the hard, slippery things in life being set aside, or even lost in summertime lightness. In this case the comparative shortness of the middle line works in that it emphasizes the difficulties (represented by the possibly warty bullfrog) that have slipped away. Nice use of "s" sounds. ~kk

This haiku to me is simply "real", and bullfrogs are definitely "slippery" creatures. I can also empathize with the writer's dismay of not being able to hold on to said frog, and yet I enjoyed the humor. So many things in life simply "slip-away", which is what makes this particular piece so profound, especially having been composed by a younger author. ~an'ya

shifting shadows
deep in the hills
a dog barks

Allison McCrossen
School of the Arts, Age 13,
Rochester, NY

This poem presents a shaded, thought-provoking landscape… slightly mysterious. I like the middle line pivot which makes sense with the first and also with the final line. The use of sound, a bark, far away, makes for an eerie feeling. Here the mood is re-enforced by the image. ~kk

Right off in line one, I'm intrigued about the "shifting shadows", then line two draws me in even further, (deep into the hills), and just when I'm right on the very edge of this haiku, "a dog barks", startling me back into reality. Skillfully vague enough to be thereby effective as a haiku moment. ~an'ya

It is refreshing to find the underused senses of taste and touch here. Also, the reader's senses are jarred awake with the sharpness of the cold water and its acrid flavor. This well-written poem leads the mind to ponder about mountain streams, hiking and even a little philosophy about letting go when life gets bitter. ~kk

What person has not thought this very thing when drinking from a mountain stream? The taste of pure water is so unknown to us anymore that it does taste shockingly metallic. Not to mention that mountain streams are always really cold. This is a well-crafted haiku that has juxtaposition, natural alliteration, and unbelievably incorporates four out of five senses, which not many old-time haiku poets are even able to do! There's taste, touch, sight, and the sound of the stream as well. ~an'ya

metallic taste
the cold stream spills
from my hand

Jenny Zhang
*Cedar Shaols High School, Age 16,
Athens, GA*

This is a haiku that some would say has bent the rules. However, it does show us as readers a very unique way of looking at an otherwise common situation, which is what a successful haiku should do. Had I been critiquing this one, I would suggest that the author perhaps might consider using an em-dash after "koi", or perhaps even consider combining lines one and two, making room for a wide setting in line one. Keep up the good work. ~an'ya

In a novel and arresting way, we know that this poet has made a wish on a copper coin and tossed it into a pool of carp. We also know that a carp in investigating the coin. All in 5 words. I wonder, as maybe the writer wonders, will this affect the outcome of the wish? I agree with an'ya that another image would perfect the verse… juxtaposing with this very original and already intriguing image. ~kk

koi
nibbling
my copper wish

Elizabeth Hetherington
*School of the Arts, Age 16,
Rochester, NY*

The judges for the 2003 competition were Claire Gallagher and Anne Homan.

What? None of the five haiku chosen for merit have the 5-7-5 syllable count? Although we have nothing against such structure, the poems that we honor happen not to have it. We believe that other elements are more important. These include the evocation of a moment of heightened awareness, presenting just enough detail so that the reader is enticed to finish the experience in a way that may personally resonate, and possibly a seasonal reference that deepens a poem with enriching connotations.

We also looked for interesting juxtapositions, well-thought-out word choices, fresh images, a good use of rhythm, and language that shows rather than tells — characteristics of all good poetry. We commend the large number of young people who submitted haiku to this contest. This indicates an interest in haiku and the mastery of words to communicate experience and feelings. We send a pat on the back to the many authors whose poems nearly made the finals. The five poems selected are of equal merit and are not ranked.

Our warmest congratulations to the authors of the haiku below!

~ *Claire Gallagher and Anne Homan, Judges*

The poet's keen observation is suggestive of an unknown story; the absence of extraneous detail allows the reader to imagine the circumstances and to read into it and resonate with it. Mystery that does not succumb to lack of clarity enhances this poem. The reference to a season is a traditional device that deepens the poem by calling upon the common associations we all have with a welcome "summer breeze". The soft consonant sounds provide a good flow in this poem, rather like a breeze, and there is a pleasant, unforced rhythm to the whole poem. The long vowel sounds of "breeze", "clothes", "thrown", and "over" increase the languid feeling, while the

summer breeze
the flutter of clothes
thrown over a chair

Laura Santiago
School of the Arts, Age 15, Grade 9, Rochester, NY

short vowel in "flutter" seems to mimic the breeze. We particularly liked that the poet chose the definite article "the" before "flutter"; this gives focus to the poem. The poet has made choices that produced a well-crafted poem, so well-crafted that it appears effortless.

pebbles underfoot
in the cold stream
stars

Henry Aigetsinger
School of the Arts, Age 15, Grade 9, Rochester, NY

This haiku utilizes several writing techniques that produced a winning poem. There is a strong juxtaposition of disparate images that give the poem a spark. The second line acts as a pivot line that can be read with the first line as a continuous thought with line one before a pause in thought before line three. Alternatively, a pause after line one would allow lines two and three to link in thought--nicely done. The inference of bare feet evokes early summer near a stream of snowmelt as well as other wading experiences. There is vivid sensory information; the stream-rounded jumble of pebbles is pressing into bare feet. Overhead, and reflected in the water, is the ordered array of blue-white stars. In addition, the flow of the stream around the poet's ankles might give a feel of the transience of life under stars that seem eternal. This poem reads well; there is no forced rhythm.

in front
of the meth lab
three children hopscotch

C. J. Welch
Walhert High School, Age 17, Grade 12, Dubuque, IA

In this haiku the poet chooses a moment in time that presents an interesting contrast between the sordid contemporary world of a meth lab, and the bright springtime image of children playing. The latter image brings strongly to mind E.E. Cummings' poem "in Just-" in which "bettyandisbel come dancing from hop-scotch and jump-rope and it's spring." Notice that the children in the haiku are playing in front of the meth lab—they are not afraid of the place—it is simply an accepted part of the neighborhood. The strong break in the poem after the second line not only gives the pause in rhythm that is traditionally valued in a haiku, but the poet has also neatly created a break in thought. Ending the poem with the word "hopscotch" brings the reader quietly back to dark implications—the syllables cut off quickly on the tongue. The meanings of "scotch" as a verb include "maim," "crush," and "stamp out," stark words implying perhaps how the meth lab could affect these children's lives in the future. The poet has suggested all this to the reader without actually saying, "How terrible life can be!"

The poet of this haiku has begun with the seasonal reference valued for adding resonance to a haiku. Ash Wednesday is a Christian celebration falling in late February or early March. It marks the beginning of Lent, a time of fasting, contemplation, and penitence during the days before Easter. Believers come to church on this day to receive ashes on their foreheads. But even more can be connoted from these two words. What has oc urred before Ash Wednesday? Especially in New Orleans and Rio de Janeiro, people celebrate Mardi Gras—Fat Tuesday— with high spirits and even indulgence. The poem has a pause in the rhythm after the first line; this slows the reader, allowing time to anticipate a change. With its description of a moment in time, the rest of the poem tells a story, but not a complete story—the reader is allowed to fill in the details. We imagine a large stone building—a church, even a cathedral—where the smallest sounds echo. Perhaps the author is thinking about personal intentions for Lenten sacrifice. We feel a sense of community in this moment. The congregation waits patiently in line to receive the ashes. There are no children whining, no adults whispering the latest gossip—only that reverberating cough. The poem ends nicely with the word "echoes," a word that lingers with its long "O."

Ash Wednesday
from lines of silent people
a cough echoes

Emily Cornish
School of the Arts, Age 14, Grade 8, Rochester, NY

This poet begins the haiku effectively with a traditional seasonal and time of day reference—"spring evening." The sun has set, but the stars are not out yet. This may be during daylight savings time, when the evening is longer and easier to savor. After a nice break in thought, the second line begins a mini story. It is raining hard and soaking through a newspaper. The third line gives us a little surprise—the newspaper is not in a gutter or on a lawn, but on someone's head! Now we have more ideas and questions to add to the story. Did the person carelessly forget an umbrella or never bother with one; did the day begin, as spring days often do, with a sunny, cloudless morning and surprise him/her with spring's changeful nature? This poem illustrates an excellent choice by the poet of a moment in the stream of experience. The poet leads us to further implications, as the transient daily news dissolves in a life-giving spring rain.

spring evening
rain soaks through the newspaper
on my head

Laura Santiago
School of the Arts, Age 15,
Grade 9, Rochester, NY

The judges for the 2002 competition were Raffael DeGruttola and Judson Evans.

We read and reread the entries separately, then got together and compared our favorites. We discussed these, compared, and finally agreed on the following selections.

~ *Raffael DeGruttola and Judson Evans*

We like several things about this haiku. The language is fresh and recreates a subtle seasonal perception with its sense of silence in a very early spring morning. The gnats seem to materialize out of the damp earth. The shape of the poem on the page reinforces the poet's observation, as the reader recognizes the way the "over" in the first line's "hovering" rests just above "over" in the second line. The poem interestingly connects the stillness and solidity of the underlying "damp earth" with the almost electric movement of the gnats.

hovering
over a damp field
a cloud of gnats

Colin Murray
*School of the Arts, Grade 8,
Rochester, NY*

This haiku combines two phenomena about the given moment, the way dust moves haphazardly yet in patterns the wind creates and how a shaft of light in the early morning can capture a lively scene. A photographer friend once said to me that there is something magical about the early morning light when objects are seen so distinctly. In the eyes of the young writer the dust moves gracefully across a field or meadow and the sun's light reflects its every move.

dawn
dust dances
on shafts of sunlight

Shannon Ryan
*School of the Arts, Grade 9,
Rochester, NY*

summer dusk
throwing stones
through a broken window

Travis Moore
School of the Arts, Grade 9,
Rochester, NY

With this haiku we are taken
to the other end of the day when the young person's
mischievous nature begins to play havoc in the
covering blanket of evening. One wonders if the broken
window was the result of the first stone thrown or was
the window already broken? We hope for the latter;
however, boys will be boys, as they say, and windows
are just another entry into the world of the night.
Again, we can imagine a city lot with an abandoned
building where more than one window has already
fallen to youthful play. How many of us remember the
days of the slingshot when distance and accuracy went
hand in hand.*

on an old
cemetery stone
my name

James Isaak
Wahlert High School, Grade 12,
Dubuque, IA

*Here we have, to quote the Proustian phrase,
"remembrance of things past," where we see our
family name from generations before on a gravestone.
There's a certain ambivalence about this fact.
Am I really related to this person? Is this just a
coincidence? And, if I am related how much do I
know about this person? It's all in the mystery of not
knowing that keeps the charm of this senryu. For the
young person, there is a fascination in knowing that
somebody with the same name once lived in this city,
and if for no other reason, I am alive and must carry
on the tradition.*

mountain stream
trout dart
around watercress

Cory Hanson
Wahlert High School, Grade 11,
Dubuque, IA

*A true outdoors person is here proclaimed.
Accompanying dad and/or grandfather by rising early
in the morning to venture out to the wilderness. Then
following the stream to where the trout are jumping.
Sitting on a rock watching as father throws his line out
and slowly reels it in hoping for a catch. The watercress
acts as a cover, which makes the adventure that much
more intriguing. You can sense the excitement in the
moment.*

Monday morning
kicking the slush
from behind the wheels

Colin Murray
School for the Arts, Grade 8,
Rochester, NY

We were fascinated by the use
of the word "slush" here. In the summer it connotes
something refreshing; however, in winter it's a
nuisance. Of course, Monday morning is the beginning
of the workweek and you want to start the day without
any inconveniences. Removing the slush in the quickest
way from the mudguards means kicking it free and
climbing into your car with dirty and wet shoes.
That feeling of disgust is conveyed with determined
abruptness.*

2001

The judges for the 2001 competition were Randy and Shirley Brooks.

We enjoyed reading the submissions to the Virgilio competition for 2001. We admired the straightforward language of these haiku and were especially drawn to the playful irony of their observations.

~ *Randy & Shirley Brooks*

In this haiku we are taken back to the perspective of a child, drawn to a window pane by the wind. It is chilly outside and a storm is brewing. The child is so close that their breath fogs the glass further clouding the vision of what's happening "out there". We don't see this as a sinister or fearful moment, but rather an instance of just wanting to see. Next, the child will be drawing or writing a word in the fogged glass.

autumn wind
rattles the glass —
a child's breath

Travis Moore
School of the Arts, Age 13, Grade 8, Rochester, NY

We like how this haiku features children in the pumpkin patch. Their faces are aglow with the excitement of Halloween as they seek the perfect pumpkin. They imagine the jack-o-lantern they could carve from each one, seeing an ear or furrowed frown in the shapes of orange skin. Their faces are aglow— so alive—with possibilities.

walking
the pumpkin patch —
children's faces aglow

Brooke Erschen
Wahlert High School, Age 18, Grade 12, Dubuque, IA

from the tanning salon
to her car
January chill

Deborah Meyer
Wahlert High School, Age 18,
Grade 12, Dubuque, IA

In the middle of winter how else can someone work on their tan? Maybe they are planning a spring break getaway to a beach and want to be ready. However, the reality is that it is still winter as she is reminding on her way back to the car after a relaxing tanning session.

strep throat
she kisses him
anyway

Heidi Streit
Walhert High School, Age 17,
Grade 12, Dubuque, IA

We love this senryu. What a hoot. Teenage love. The invincible, fearless youth, willing to risk all for a kiss. This is the kiss he or she has dreamed of for weeks. Nothing will stop it now. Not even strep throat. This senryu works so well because it starts with "strep throat" so she knows what she is "getting into". The anyway suggests a slight, perhaps flippant, risk analysis that is ignored. Sometimes we just have to face the consequences, the inevitability, that love is a risky business. On the other hand, kissing someone with strep throat is just stupid (from a grown-up's perspective).

after the dentist appointment
sister returns
all smiles

Katherine Welter
Wahlert High School,
Age 17, Dubuque, IA

We liked the simplicity of this haiku. Sister is showing off her clean teeth. Perhaps she was not so eager to go to the dentist, afraid she might have cavities. However, now it's over. She got a clean bill of health from the dentist. Look Ma, no cavities!

new beau
fingering the tattoo
with her name

Kali Smith
Wahlert High School, Age 16,
Grade 11, Dubuque, IA

We like the excitement of new love in this senryu. He has shown his commitment with a new tattoo with her name. Everything's new and exciting... and intimate as she fingers the tattoo. Did it hurt? Is it still sore? Next thing you know she will be kissing him, even if he has strep throat!

2000

The judges for the 2000 competition were Ruth Yarrow and Kathleen Decker.

We feel honored to have this chance to share moments in your lives. Many submissions had the snap and humor of senryu, but since this is a haiku contest, we didn't choose them. We chose the haiku that for us evoked emotion, as we've tried to sketch in our comments. We find that fresh images, often two that reverberate with each other, work best. You don't need to summarize your experience in the last line—readers can share what you're feeling simply from the way you capture the experience. If yours was not one of the six we finally chose, please know that other judges may well have chosen different ones, and don't be discouraged. Know that your poems were read and enjoyed, and that you have ahead of you a life of moments to capture. We hope you all keep writing!

~ Ruth Yarrow and Kathleen Decker

There's a freshness about this bright green haiku that captures the essence of spring. You can see where she stepped because the tender grass is squashed down, and the dew drops knocked off. But it's a light, transitory step, just as the season itself is light and transitory. The step took just a moment, the length of a haiku. The poet has captured the feeling of this moment and the whole season in a few words.
~Yarrow

This poem has captured a fleeting moment, and the beauty of a beloved's footsteps, in very few words. There is an optimism in the implied word play on spring morning, and springy step (leaving the imprint of her step). ~Decker

spring morning
the dewy grass
holds the shape of her step

Nathaniel B. Gach
Marple Newtown High School,
Age 18, Grade 12,
Newtown Square, PA

Thanksgiving Dinner
Silence, and the
pendulum swinging

Dave Ferry
*Marple Newtown High School, Age
17, Grade 12, Newtown Square, PA*

*This moment of silence, probably the grace before
the meal, feels heavy and ponderous, like the
pendulum of a grandfather clock. We can feel that
strong emotions exist between family members.
While the family is still for a moment, the poet is
suddenly aware of the movement of the pendulum.
Paradoxically, while this special moment is
frozen like a snapshot, time moves on. The next
Thanksgiving will not be the same; individual family
members may come or go, and each may change.
One thing is certain--they will all be older, because
the pendulum is swinging. The poet has captured
the contrast between stillness and movement in one
moment. ~Yarrow*

*This had a different feel for me—I felt that the
poet might have been capturing extreme tension.
Thanksgiving, a time of joy and plenty, is suddenly
arrested and held captive by silence. Perhaps no one
dares to speak, or a faux pas has been committed,
and the conversation is arrested. ~Decker*

a whale's last call
the blue sea —
red

Elizabeth Frank
*Wahlert High School, Age 17,
Grade 12, Dubuque, IA*

*Contrasts enrich this haiku. First is the obvious
contrast between the translucent blue waters and
the opaque red blood. The whale's last call contrasts
with the silence of death. Its call reaches out while its
death closes in. The enormity of the whale and the
distances in the sea contrast with the close immediate
wound. The poet, in a few words, gives us a life and
its end. ~Yarrow*

*I have little to add to this elegant comment except
that the contrast in the warm color of life, the sea,
(blue) is laid in stark contrast to the red of death and
I find this exceptionally well done for a student of
haiku. ~Decker*

The poet might have just walked on by, barely noticing the hole in the wall, let alone what lies on the other side. But he or she stopped and let the neutral colors of cool stone frame the bright colors of flaming autumn. The "aw" alliteration in "autumn afternoon" and the "oh" sounds in "hole in the stone wall" are a perfect frame for the feeling of appreciating beauty that pervades this haiku. ~Yarrow

This haiku reminds us of the process of writing haiku--to stop and examine the moment, and to glory in its simplicity. In my mind, the author was hurrying past the wall, and was stopped by the view through the wall. A lover, or perhaps just a distant landscape, suddenly enriched by its quaint frame. ~Decker

autumn afternoon
hole in the stone wall
a perfect frame

Nathaniel B. Gach
*Marple Newtown High School,
Age 18, Grade 12,
Newtown Square, PA*

The poet submitted this in capital letters, which may indicate how he or she felt about this special moment. We feel it works just as well in lower case, so have taken the liberty to write it this way. In just the fleeting moment that it takes a bat to fly, it appears to have linked the great distance from Orion's stars to the moon. Two cold bright distant points in the night sky are joined by a warm, dark, near fellow mammal. ~Yarrow

I particularly enjoyed the contrast between the bat, and the immensity of the dark night sky. Of course, it is impossible to fly from Orion to the moon, but the bat is impossibly small next to the stars, and it is that contrast which is endearing, and striking. ~Decker

from Orion
a bat flits
to the moon

Thomas Murray
*School of the Arts, Age 15, Grade 9,
Rochester, NY*

mountain view photo
capturing
the tourist's breath

Kate Chapman
Wahlert High School, Age 18,
Grade 12, Dubuque, IA

A photograph is taken in an instant and captures an image. This haiku on the surface simply describes that picture. The poet, though, has written more than a matter-of-fact description. We can tell it's cold on the mountain, because the tourist's warm breath has condensed in the chilly mountain air. We can guess that the tourist may have climbed and is breathing hard. But most importantly, the emotion slips through. We can feel the tourist's deep breath as she or he takes in the majesty of the scene, and then exhales in awe at its beauty. Not just the photo but the mountain itself has captured the tourist's breath. ~Yarrow

There is another way to look at this moment. Perhaps the tourist's breath has given the mountain a faint haze in the photo. So perhaps the tourist's breath has given another dimension to the mountain in the photo, and they have added some mystery to the scene as it was captured on film. ~Decker

1999

The judges for the 1999 competition were Yvonne Hardenbrook and Cherie Hunter Day.

Many of this year's entries required more than one look and some discussion. As judges, we looked objectively for well-crafted pieces with special attention to word choice and line breaks that hinted at a deeper meaning. We also had to consider the subjective criteria of memories and emotions that these haiku/senryu evoked for us. Those elements were much harder to evaluate, but we were able to narrow our choices to six poems. We thank all the poets and teachers for their fine efforts and hope they continue to study and practice the genre.

~ Yvonne Hardenbrook and Cherie Hunter Day

We looked for the clear image that hints at a deeper meaning and creates a space for the reader as well. Both judges grew up with farmer fathers whose hands really did show the work—callused hands with thick fingers, gloveless even in winter. Farming by hand today is almost a lost art, so we appreciate the poem, and the poet's keen insight and clean craftsmanship.

farming
his hands
showing the work

Damian Stork
Wahlert High School, Age 18,
Grade 12, Dubuque, IA

In televised marathons or local high school track events, we have seen for ourselves the concentration necessary for these athletes to succeed. The poet brings home the power of the moment by neatly juxtaposing the intense expression on the runner's face with the disgust that surely follows the realization of being shat upon. This surprise is conveyed perfectly in the poem's third line.

concentration
on the runner's forehead
birdpoop

Heather Klinthammer
Wahlert High School, Age 18,
Grade 12, Dubuque, IA

at the movie
their hands meet...
in the buttered popcorn

Paula Faber
Wahlert High School, Age 18,
Grade 12, Dubuque, IA

More senryu than haiku, this poem seems quite appropriate to teen life full of irony, frustration, mistaken signals, blind groping, and good humor. Whether on a first date, hoping to touch each other, or steady date just hungry for popcorn, the poet has captured the moment with a wry sense of humor.

mother's crossed arms
a reminder —
of our argument

Heather Klinthammer
Wahlert High School, Age 18,
Grade 12 , Dubuque, IA

No psychology lesson needed to recognize a parent's crossed arms as "end of discussion." At a very young age we become masters of body language, and we found this poet masterful in portraying the scene with few words and well-chosen line breaks.

Overhead projector
the lesson
over a student's head

Joe Arling
Wahlert High School, Age 17, Grade
12, Dubuque, IA

At first, this senryu seems to state the obvious, but the skillful play on words in the third line adds delightful humor. By folding the meaning back on itself, the poet invites us to linger in the scene and enjoy the pun.

after the rain
so visible
the spider's web

Tony Leisen
Wahlert High School, Age 18,
Grade 12, Dubuque, IA

This haiku is centered in summer with the season word or kigo, "spider's web." The words resonate and seem to tangle the mind. How can we be aware of things that are there and yet not there? This poem has a quality similar to a Zen koan.

1998

The judges for the 1998 competition were Ellen Compton and Jeff Witkin.

We have chosen poems that have one quality in common: they draw the reader into the moment—telling neither too much nor too little—leaving room for the reader to reflect on his/her own experience. Congratulations to the poets.

~ *Ellen Compton and Jeff Witkin*

Haiku-like, the photograph captures a single moment in a world given increasingly to activity. Perhaps the photo is a "still" taken from filmed motion—a dance performance or the flight of a hawk, for example. Or might the stillness be in the posing for the photo?
~*Compton*

A snapshot of the way things are, when seen clearly, stops us and puts us firmly in eternity. The poet at the flashpoint sees the connection between people, objects, and occasions that are in and outside of the photo here, sees their past and their future; as the film gathers its light, the poetic vision brings the poet home. ~*Witkin*

photograph:
for a moment
everything still

Tyler Stoffel
Wahlert High School, Age 18,
Grade 12, Dubuque, IA

The smile across time is tinged with sadness. As our own face is seen in a pond, the poet sees through many years, many changes, and from the silty bottom, a smile rises to the clean surface of the moment. We wonder about the relationship between these two, but it is the linking of the poet with the here and now that brings the poem its gleam. ~*Witkin*

Has the smiled-at managed into sourness, or become ill? Has the relationship changed or ended? This is a poem of delicate understatement—one that suggests the poet's longing and offers many possibilities as to its cause. ~*Compton*

smiling at him
in the old pictures
he smiles back

Crystal Wagner
Wahlert High School, Age 17,
Grade 11, Dubuque. IA

the quiet girl
wearing
a loud shirt

Tara Stecklein
Wahlert High School, Age 18,
Grade 12, Dubuque, IA

A moment of heightened perception, in which one external (the shirt) lets the poet look beyond another external (the girl's apparent quietness) to perceive the girl within. ~Compton

The contrast shocks us into awareness that things are not always as they seem. The child never heard is finally seen in all her complexities and contradictions of ourselves. Regardless of who chose the shirt, the girl who wears it now comes boldly to life. ~Witkin

finding myself
between the willows —
autumn evening

Adam Rauch
Marple Newtown Senior High School,
Age 17, Grade 12,
Newtown Square, PA

Stopping on an evening walk the poet finds himself between two willows. The trees will soon shed their leaves, the coolness gives a sense of winter. Deeply felt is all that has been lost. At the same time the willows will bring forth their leaves again in spring. For the moment the poet and the willows are one. ~Witkin

Like the autumn evening, the poem is bitter-sweet. The poet's experience might recall similar times in one's own autumn walks, often over unplanned routes, frequently lost in thought—only to arrive in a familiar place without being quite sure how one got there. The leaves are turning, dusk comes early. In beauty there is just a little pain. ~Compton

signs of spring —
tanktop revealing
her butterfly tattoo

Dani DeCaro
Marple Newtown Senior High
School, Age 16, Grade 12,
Newtown Square, PA

A gently humorous moment. One senses not only the poet's joy in the signs of spring, but also the joy of the tanktop wearer in her new freedom. Might they be the same person? Nice rhythm in this poem especially the tanktop/tattoo interplay. ~Compton

The lightness of the poem flutters delicately past the butterfly and then ends. The consonance of tanktop with tattoo reinforces what we feel only at the last word. A time of renewal and the warm spring sun brings freshness and play and yet the tanktop wearer, perhaps still quite young, has heard at least a note or two from the songs of experience. The interplay of the unfolding of spring and the unfolding of the wings of youth make poetry out of what could have been cute word play. ~Witkin

A simple description. Watching this miracle, the poet sees her own life, all life, as part of the cosmic lattice. The changing patterns, all of them beautiful, hold for a moment an understanding of the mystery behind it all. In the season for reflection on change, there is a profound sense of awe in this vision. ~Witkin

A meditative poem that speaks of the specialness of "nothing special," and of the ephemeral nature of all things. The poet has perceived a grace in every-day shapes constantly forming and re-forming into patterns, no two ever the same. ~Witkin

leaf pattern
arranged
rearranged by the wind

Bridget Leary
Wahlert High School, Age 18,
Grade 12, Dubuque IA

1997

The Virgilio Contest for 1997 was suspended while the deadline date for entries was changed from autumn to spring in order to fit better with the school year.

1996

The judges for the 1996 competition were Lee Gurga and Paul Mena.first snow

the whole pomegranate
one seed at a time

Margaret Miller
Hopewell Valley Central High School,
Age 17, Grade 12, Pennington, NJ

first date
her dog
likes me

Scott Splinter
Wahlert High School, Age 17,
Grade 12, Dubuque, IA

silence I wait
for the starter's pistol

Bryan Roberts
Waialua High School, Age 16,
Grade 10, Waialua, HI

dark street
a lit cigarette
moves closer

Brian Mulligan
Wahlert High School, Age 18,
Grade 12,

Dubuque, IA

rain
finding
the hole in my shoe

Adam Dodds
Wahlert High School Dubuque,
Age 18, Grade 12, Dubuque, IA

Halloween
my feelings
behind a mask

Krista Dodds
Wahlert High School, Age 16,
Grade 11, Dubuque, IA

1995

The judge for the 1995 competition was Paul O. Williams.

Over 325 poems were entered in this year's Virgilio Competition. It was a difficult task to narrow the selection down to just seven. While a majority of the poems submitted could best be classified as minimal, some were five words or fewer, or senryu, concerned solely with human situations--often humorous, we were looking for poems that captured a haiku moment--a specific place and time, recorded honestly, free from commentary or sentimentality, with a lasting resonance of deeper understanding. I want to emphasize that every young poet that submitted work is to be congratulated and encouraged to continue writing.

~ *Paul O. Williams*

This swimmer is setting out in the morning, with all the associations of beginning. He or she is having an effect--even on the sun's reflection, a part, a focal part, of the scene. The swimmer recalls Whitman's solitary singer, the mockingbird, also associated with water. The poem suggests a bravery, an assertive action, a proclamation of the swimmer's being, declaring his or her being in the world.

solitary swimmer
ripples
   the early-morning sun

Anne Alfredo
*Wahlert High School, 9th Grade,
Dubuque, IA*

Obviously, the old man is not reeling in the sea, except in whimsical perceptions. But he isn't reeling in anything else either, and he is absorbing the whole atmosphere of the shore, and that is most of the point of fishing anyhow. Being at the sea is the point, reeling it into one's being. Fishing is the excuse. How is it that so many surf fishers are older men? This example fits the scene.

old man
  reeling in
 the sea

Beth Paisley
*Wahlert High School, 9th Grade,
Dubuque, IA*

after the flood
   our flag waves
      from the clothesline

Katie O'Connor
Wahlert High School, 9th Grade,
Dubuque, IA

A poem of recovery, of going on, this haiku is about setting things right again, showing the flag, even if it is, at the moment, mostly drying out. It is still there, still waving, and it is "our" flag, not just any flag. It is a step to reestablishment, in recovery. Its colors are clear and bright, declaring hope.

---

dandelion
wished
away

Tony Leisen
Wahlert High School, 9th Grade,
Dubuque, IA

Dandelions are so easy to dissipate with one puff almost as slight as a wish, and the puff makes just that sound—wish—as the seeds float down the wind. The poem is economical. contains a delightful onomatopoeia and is altogether pleasing.

---

the tree
snowcovered
except one leaf

Maureen Reilly
Wahlert High School, 9th Grade,
Dubuque, IA

There is always that leaf, that exception, that different thing, being itself, separate, individual. Such single leaves give the world distinctiveness. Again, the poem is economical, coming at the end into the sharp focus of its perception.

---

two oak leaves
just the same
until a brown moth flies away

Charlotte Stevenson
Castilleja School, 9th Grade,
Palo Alto, CA

Protective coloration is such a dry expression, drier, perhaps, than the leaf itself, or the moth, which startles us with its suddenly becoming itself, flying with a living purpose and not at the whim of the breeze. It is a separate will we are dealing with, asserting itself in its flight.

---

two bold streaks of blue
   split by the thin horizon —
ocean and spring sky

Katie Gallagher
University High School,
10th Grade, Honolulu, HI

All that blue… only one defining line, the horizon, gives us shape and definition, sets the world on a level again. The poem is a 5-7-5 haiku, the only one among our winners. Its longer center line becomes the horizon, with its final dash lining it out, right in the middle of the scene.

The judges for the 1994 competition were Christopher Herold and June Hymas.

More than a quarter of the 450 entries in this year's contest were exceptionally good. It is interesting to note that, although this event is a haiku contest, a vast majority of the entries were pure senryu. Nature, other than human nature, was a mere footnote. Nevertheless, the sensitivity demonstrated by these young poets is astounding. We wish there were space to praise a good many more. Nearly all of the haiku submitted were not only written in the free-form style, but were of the minimalist school, many with a single word constituting a line.

In choosing the winners, we looked for originality, interpenetration, clarity, and concreteness of images, focus on the present instant, and skill with words. Overall, we sought, especially, a sense of the deeper spirit of haiku.

The haiku teacher and the ninth-grade class at Wahlert High School in Dubuque, Iowa, are sure to celebrate, having swept all honors in this year's contest. Since there were only a few high schools whose students submitted work, we hope that more will be done in the future to promote haiku, and to encourage participation in the Nicholas Virgilio contest.

~ *Christopher Herold and June Hymas*

The seasonal reference of this poem is clear; the time when potatoes are harvested. Other than potatoes, what treasure will the shovel unearth, maybe a coveted bone? At some level, does Lisa's dog recognize its own nature in that of the shovel, much as haiku poets recognize themselves through heightened awareness of "external" phenomena? The poet may well have been mulling over this very question. In doing what her dog does so well, dig, she finds significance in a common activity, significance that might otherwise have gone unnoticed: the unearthing of simple treasures, and a realization of a deeper connection to her dog, perhaps in the same way that her dog felt a connection to the shovel.

digging potatoes
my dog barks
at the shovel

Lisa Tranel
Wahlert High School, 9th Grade, Dubuque, IA

**pheasant hunting
his hand too cold
to pull the trigger**

Adam Asbury
*Wahlert High School, 9th Grade,
Dubuque, IA*

*We feel the bitter cold of this poem, the coldness
that was to end with the taking of life. The actual
split-second of "freezing-up" is the point of focus. So
sudden, the single explosion, a pheasant's wings…
deafening, the silence where a gunshot could have
been.*

mountains the horizon

Brooke Althaus
*Wahlert High School, 9th Grade,
Dubuque, IA*

*The poem is not "I see mountains along the horizon,"
or "mountains are the horizon," or any other re-write.
It's not only that the single horizontal line suggests
the horizon, although that is the case. As we live
with this poem, we find that it continually expands.
"Mountains" is a rich word, associated with snow,
rock, trees, stillness, storms, the purple shadows,
and so forth. As we move through this cluster of
meanings, we come to "the horizon" which always
surrounds us. It is a difficult path ahead, no matter
which way we go. It won't be a flat, easy walk.*

**turning the corner
he turns his hat
in a different direction**

Nate Jenkins
*Wahlert High School, 9th Grade,
Dubuque, IA*

*A simple act, a natural act, perhaps an unconscious
one. Adaptability is a strong human characteristic.
Here are two possible scenarios, each powerful
in its own way: (1) A teenager leaves home for
school, baseball cap worn in the more conventional
manner, as his parents insist upon seeing it. But,
when he turns the corner, he assumes his image of
choice, turning the cap backwards as is the custom
of his friends. The rebellion of youth is universal;
it has always been. (2) A teenager leaves home,
baseball cap worn in the conventional way, and
reaches the corner. It is a brisk day and there is a
stiff breeze… rounding the corner, he turns his cap
so that it will not be taken by the wind. He is in tune
with his environment and takes charge of his life.
Adaptability--whether to social environment or to
the weather.*

Even those who may not be familiar with this rite are likely to understand this poem. The image is stark and clear; the poet's recognition of the need to be unburdened of sin, of guilt, is expressed more by the dirty palm than by the Eucharist itself. It is the contrast that underlines this need and deepens the impression.

Eucharist
white
on my dirty palm

Jessi Kurt
Wahlert High School, 9th Grade,
Dubuque, IA

The ellipsis holds us for a moment in the first awareness of rain. It is possible that the rain is so light that hands are held out to be sure. This is a common reaction, often an involuntary one. Alternatively, the person holding out his hands may know that it has started to rain and welcome it, palms up, a willing participation—a celebration.

rain...
he holds out
his hands

Amanda Wetjen
Wahlert High School, 9th Grade,
Dubuque, IA

As we grow older, those things that once fascinated or gave pleasure tend to exert less of a hold on us. Exuberance gives way to calmness, laughter to a smile (sometimes merely a polite smile). Often we grow weary, even in the company of friends and relatives, and it becomes less and less important to conceal our true feelings. This poem acknowledges and accepts the universal seasons of life.

grandmother's smile
spreads
into a yawn

Lisa White
Wahlert High School, 9th Grade ,
Dubuque, IA

1993

The judges for the 1993 competition were Tom Clausen and Jack Ervin.

The 1993 Virgilio Haiku Contest for High School students received 350 entries of which at least 70 were worthy of recognition. The judges were hard pressed to narrow selections to seven entries only. It was a real privilege and pleasure to share the experiences and moments that were carefully recorded in each of the entries. The gamut of life experiences was well represented in the range of entries. Keen expressions of direct observations, nature, connection, love, heartache, loss, alienation, humor, joy and simple moments of beauty and poignancy were included. We sincerely hope that everyone who entered will continue to read and write, with their senses open and aware of the poetry that exists anywhere, anytime.

We would like to thank all the teachers who contributed their encouragement and assistance with the Virgilio contest. There were so many other entries that deserved commentary. Our only regret as judges is that we cannot individually comment on them.

~ Tom Clausen and Jack Ervin

Without telling us what or how to feel this poet invites us into a quiet space that requires us as the reader to supply the reaction. Do we feel small, alone, afraid, cold, warm, secure, cozy, separated, remote or happy with a bit of peace? Haiku often require that we as readers participate in and engage with the experience so that we are placed in a setting similar to that which the writer wrote from but with freedom to form our own response. This haiku paints us into a bedroom corner of a silent house and it's up to us to feel exactly what this conjures.

In the corner
of my bedroom
in the silent house

Robin Grady
*Wahlert High School, Age 14,
Grade 9, Dubuque, IA*

I watch myself
walking
past the still lake

Cory Olson
Wahlert High School, Age 14
Grade 9, Dubuque, IA

When nature provides a still moment, we are given a golden opportunity to see ourselves, whether in reflection literally or in thoughts. The allowance of thoughts on a walk and then the actual reflection on the lake surface serve to highlight the bridge between our conscious and unconscious realms. There is an element of narcissism implied here too in that what this writer has focused on is their own self-image. How human a tendency it is to reflect and be self-referential even while out in the pristine beauty of our natural world. The tranquility of the lake might extend to us the chance to see something we could not see in more turbulent times. We are left to ponder the dreamlike reflection that mirrors us as we walk along.

emergency room:
watching the spider
cross the floor

Keith Habel
Wahlert High School, Age 14,
Grade 9, Dubuque, IA

Trapped by circumstances from which one cannot extricate oneself or replay, this poem captures the helplessness of being in the midst of an emergency. The shock of such a situation heightens awareness or transfixes us and tends to make us see more than we might ordinarily. Haiku often arrive when we notice or feel something that pinpoints or suggests what is most telling and poetic in the moment. For many people the sight of a spider is possibly unwelcome. That this spider appears in the sterile surroundings of an emergency room strengthens this poem's evocation of what is intuitively known. That being that nowhere in life is control absolute. Just as emergencies happen- -spiders appear in sterile environments. There are situations where all we can do is watch.

goodnight embrace
by the dusty road —
all the stars

Becky Atkinson
Eastern Alamance High School,
Age 17, Grade 12, Mebane, NC

Universal themes are juxtaposed and utilized to strengthen the emotions of a parting in the night. A goodnight embrace against such essential elements as the dust and stars helps us to understand the feeling and empowerment that this moment is all about.

The earthquake as the great equalizer is one of nature's most dramatic events. This poem links a huge event with a tiny detail which in essence signifies the poetic tables of life being turned, which can be so true in a disaster. That the knight knocks into the king is a telling commentary on what may be happening to the whole kingdom. The reality that an outside event might affect an inside situation identifies the resonance of chain reactions that constantly is taking place.

earthquake…
on the chess table
the horse hits the king

Pascu Dumitru
*School No. 39, Age 13, Grade 6,
Constanta, Romania*

There is something about dolls that evokes many different emotions. This poem has a haunting feel to it as if the box were perhaps confining this doll. Being shoeless emphasizes that this doll is being studied and this detail clues us in to considering what poetry requires of us. Is the doll shoeless from being played with and put away hastily or is it propped in this state staring out ready to walk out of its box?

Inside the box
sits a doll
shoeless

Noelle Egan
*Cherry Hill High School, age 16,
Grade 11, West Cherry Hill, NJ*

What has captured this poet's attention is the contrast of patterns. A sense that the crisscrossing of the net has resulted in this fish's capture serves to enhance the pattern of the fish. Anything caught tends to evince a detailed look that creates a distinct lasting impression.

striped fish
criss-crossed
by a salty net

Heather Caulberg
*Eastern Alamance High School,
Age 16, Grade 11, Mebane, NC*

The judges for the 1992 competition were Carol Purington and Kathleen R. O'Toole.

In this third year of the contest conducted in memory of Nicholas A. Virgilio, the number of entries again increased significantly. Well over 500 haiku were sent in by students from 15 schools in 9 states in the USA (Iowa, Missouri, New Jersey, New Mexico, New York, North Carolina, Pennsylvania, Texas, Wisconsin) and students in Mexico and Romania.

The level of technical maturity displayed by these young writers is impressive. Precise, vivid images, handled with economy and objectivity, present subjects ranging from dull lectures to drunken fathers, from babies to sunsets to AIDS to Christmas trees. One-, two-, and four-line formats are experimented with, as are minimalist and visual techniques.

The seven winning haiku, chosen from dozens of fine poems, honor the standard of excellence set by the late Nick Virgilio. Our congratulations to writers and teachers!

~ *Carol Purington and Kathleen R. O'Toole*

Auditory and visual images are skillfully blended in this haiku. We clap to the voices, we sway with the bodies. And in one way, singers and dancers are in rhythm: the strong beat of the voices is felt and followed by the moving feet. Yet we perceive, as well, the broken rhythm of a tourist's world in which Native Americans do not dance to their own music and white men dance to words they do not understand.

indian chant
only white men
dancing

Chris McQuillen
*Wahlert High School, Age 14,
Grade 9, Dubuque, IA*

The serenity of this haiku draws the reader away to a brief rest in a beautiful spot. One's eyes follow the swirlings of colorful butterflies, and for a few moments there is no noise, no rush, no tension.

butterflies in the air
in the herbarium
deep silence

Diana Stanciu
Constanta, Romania

silent study hall:
my stomach growls
anyway

Cindy Stierman
Wahlert High School, Age 17,
Grade 12, Dubuque, IA

Sometimes, even when you want to go along with the rule-makers, the body just won't cooperate. Sound effects and timing are wonderful here— the hush imposed by those three initial "s's," the onomatopoeic explosion of "growl," then the hesitation of that telling third line.

After his funeral,
the white line
on her tanned finger.

David Sickler
Wyoming Valley West High School,
Age 16, Grade 11, Plymouth, PA

This subject almost defies the restraint required in haiku. The writer succeeds by use of the austere contrast between white skin and tanned finger. That pale band somehow conveys the emotional blankness that follows the funeral of someone who shouldn't have left us.

I and the dog
hunting together
the evening mosquitoes

Olivia Diana Bangal
Secondary School, Age 14,
Constanta, Romania

An end-of-the day outing with a good companion turns into an encounter with other predators. The unexpected reversal of roles, along with the relaxed tone and flow of images, distinguish this light-hearted piece.

out of sight
            o
      ballo n
and the child's smile

Ben Meier
Wahlert High School, Age 15,
Grade 9, Dubuque, IA

Oh, we say, when we see an escaped balloon, and that is literally what the reader of this visual haiku says. This admirable poem employs a balloon to show us the loss of something as evanescent as balloons—a child's joy.

Inside its shell
    a snail
    and rain…

Yezmin Soberanes Albert
Hamilton School, Age 17, Grade 11,
Mexico D.F., Mexico

With a handful of words the poet gives us not only the snail's world of shell and rain, but also that place in our own particular world where snails shine— your wet sidewalk, my damp garden path. The slant rhyme of "shell" and "snail" and the assonance of "snail" and "rain" further compact the scene.

The judges for the 1991 competition were Joyce Walker Currier and Michael Dylan Welch.

The 1991 Virgilio Haiku Contest for High School students, sponsored by the Haiku Society of America, received 307 entries. As judges, we looked for quality, freshness, and originality, and felt that the poems we selected should be complete, needing no further refinement. Our selections are given below, including eight honorable mentions (in ranked order) by category: haiku, senryu, and two visual or concrete poems. We received many other notable submissions, and although they may not be listed here, we encourage their authors to submit them for publication. Special thanks to the teachers and schools concerned for their support--and congratulations to all the winners. Keep writing!

In closing, thank you to the Haiku Society of America, and to Garry Gay, 1991 HSA president, for the pleasure and privilege of judging this contest. It isn't easy to define haiku and senryu, and far more difficult to teach it. We encourage all students, and all teachers, in their practice and experience of haiku. As always, keep writing!

~ Joyce Walker Currier and Michael Dylan Welch

In this poem the value of the slow pace of nature is shown in the skillful and simple way the poet works with timelessness. Timelessness uses time slowly, and the writer focuses without pretense on the fullness of the creative world and records it. ~Currier

This poem is deceptively simple. We don't know where the flowers are, nor what kind of flowers open slowly in front of the poet, but we do know that the writer is still, centered, patient—and aware enough to notice the pace by which the flowers receive the light of the dawning day. Perhaps the writer is opening in the same way, slowly, to a continued life of awareness. ~Welch

As the sun rises
the flowers open
slowly...

Paola Mizrahi
Hamilton School, Age 16, Grade 11, Mexico, D.F., Mexico

new mother...
her old cat appears
at nursing time

Gina Valentine
Wahlert High School, Age 18,
Grade 12, Dubuque, IA

If you've ever lived on a farm, you know cats have a way of sensing when there's milk around. I am impressed with the integrity of the writer as she deals with and unites her subject matter "as one." Just as the old cat intuitively grasps the mystery of the senses, the poet presents it beautifully in this strikingly pure haiku. ~Currier

I especially like this haiku for its subtlety and maturity. A new baby has come to the home and demands the attention given previously to the old cat. The cat appears at nursing time, a time of closeness, of bonding. Perhaps the old cat has had kittens when it was younger and comes to the new mother as a way of expressing understanding. The contrast of young and old, the newness of the baby, the newness of the mother's experience of mothering, and the inevitable cycles of life combine to enrich this sensitive poem. Yet much is left unsaid, such as the mother's reaction to the cat now that she has a baby to nurse. The image resonates in many directions. Finally, this poem is filled with sabi, and joy, too, for the new birth. ~Welch

Blowing out
a match
the sudden smell

Jana Juergens
Wahlert High School, Age 17,
Grade 12, Dubuque, IA

Here is a haiku of sensual impression. The poet is delightfully present as the blown-out match suffuses her with the sudden recognizable smell that brings writer and reader together in our humanity. ~Currier

This is an intimate poem, an experience all of us have felt. When you are close to a match and blow it out, you easily notice its distinctive smell. Perhaps this match was used to light a birthday cake, or maybe a campfire far away in the woods. In the midst of laughter and the smell of chocolate cake—or perhaps the rich scent of pine in a dark green forest—the sudden smell of a blown-out match is indeed startling enough to deepen your awareness of your surroundings. ~Welch

**Christmas Day
the hunters
feed the deer**

Matt Richards
*Wahlert High School, Age 17,
Grade 12 , Dubuque, IA*

**Father home
late again…
my mother's eyes**

Angela Widmyer
*Wahlert High School, Age 17,
Grade 12, Dubuque, IA*

chemistry between lab partners

Noelle Bellaver
*Wahlert High School, Age 17,
Grade 12, Dubuque, IA*

"Christmas Day" is a well-crafted haiku about the fallibilities of man/hunter juxtaposed with his prey, the deer. "Father home" is a straightforward haiku of living experience that gives the reader a knowable understanding of cause and effect. And "chemistry between lab partners" is an excellent open-ended one-line haiku. ~Currier

These three poems exhibit compassion, sensitivity, freshness, and humor--the mixed emotions and unusual compassion of the hunters feeding the deer, the young person's quiet observations of her mother's eyes when her father comes home late, and the delightful word-play and double meaning of "chemistry" between two high school students in a class. Each poem suggests an untold story, and that is precisely what a good haiku should do. (Incidentally, the last of these three poems could be classified as a senryu, but I think its success as a poem is more important than how it is labeled.) ~Welch

Gina's visual haiku communicates to us the "aaahhh," and we, the readers, all see the flattened penny and imagine its untold story. Scott's haiku is a visual account of words carefully spaced to show the brokenness in and out of a relationship. ~Currier

In both of these poems, the shape or treatment of the words makes them work. Who has not laid a penny on a train track, then marveled at the weight of the train, at the penny's subsequent flatness (as shown by the "flat" look of the poem on the page)? Who has not suffered a break-up, as indicated by the separated word? These poems by their nature may not have as much depth or resonance as more conventional haiku or senryu, yet they are satisfying and accessible. We wanted to include them to show that preconceptions about haiku can indeed be successfully challenged. ~Welch

train flattened penny

Gina Valentine
*Wahlert High School, Age 18,
Grade 12, Dubuque, IA*

**re la tion ship
broken**

Scott Kluck
*Wahlert High School, Age 18, Grade
12, Dubuque, IA*

day after the big test
the nurse's office
empty

Noelle Bellave
Wahlert High School, Age 17,
Grade 12 , Dubuque, IA

beautiful girl
I turn my head and run
the red light

Matt Richards
Wahlert High School, Age 17,
Grade 12 , Dubuque, IA

out of our flavor
ice cream man
swears in Spanish

Kristin Torgler
Wahlert High School, Age 17,
Grade 12, Dubuque, IA

These three senryu are a wonderful representation
of humor and amusement. Noelle's senryu is pure
perception, Matt handles the third line deftly, and
Kristin gives us a fine blend of sound and image.
~Welch

Noelle's senryu tells a simple truth about certain
students. Kristin's shares a simple yet unexpected
experience. And Matt's poem surprises us with its
twist between the second and third lines. These are
fun, immediately accessible poems. ~Currier

1990

The judges for the 1990 competition were Harriett Bley, Minna Lerman, and vincent tripi. No commentary is available for this year.

under the tree
a planted feather

Tim Ehringer
Wahlert High School, Age 18, 12th
Grade, Dubuque, IA

Mad at myself…
the ball keeps hitting
its own shadow

Valentin Rader
Cedar Shoals High School, Age 16,
11th Grade, Athens, GA

he gives me
roses
and their thorns

Keri Haas
Wahlert High School, age 18, 12th
Grade, Dubuque, IA

beside the waterfall
the little girl
wets her pants

Jane Schueller
Wahlert High School, Age 17,
12th Grade, Dubuque, IA

I see his wholeness
through the gap
in his teeth

Andrea Stapleton
Wahlert High School, Age 17, 12th
Grade, Dubuque, IA

light of a million stars…
still
the darkness

Andy Daughetee
Wahlert High School, Age 17,
12th Grade, Dubuque, IA

awakened from sleep:
cries
of my aborted baby

Keri Haas
Wahlert High School, Age 18, 12th
Grade, Dubuque, IA

seashells
take me
from the shore

Julie Ernst
Wahlert High School, Age 17,
12th Grade, Dubuque, IA

Resources for Teaching Haiku

Last updated: July 16, 2020
© 2020, Randy Brooks

This is a bibliography of resources for teaching haiku, tanka, senryu and related haikai arts. If you have resources you would like to recommend for this bibliography, contact:

Dr. Randy Brooks
6 Madera Court, Taylorville, IL 62568
brooksbooks@gmail.com

Recommended Books

Addiss, Stephen. *The Art of Haiku: Its History Through Poems and Paintings of the Japanese Masters.* Boston & London: Shambala, 2012.

Aitken, Robert. *A Zen Wave: Bashô's Haiku & Zen.* New York and Tokyo: John Weatherhill, Inc., 1978.

Amann, Eric. *The Wordless Poem: A Study of Zen in Haiku.* Toronto, Ontario: The Haiku Society of Canada, 1978. Reprint of 1969 edition, signed.

Basho, Matsuo. Translated by Jane Reichhold. *Basho: The Complete Haiku.* New York: Kodansha International, 2008.

Basho, Matsuo. Translated by Dorothy Britton. *A Haiku Journey: Basho's Narrow Road to a Far Province.* New York: Kodansha International, 1980. Revised paperback edition.

Beichman, Janine. *Masaoka Shiki.* Boston, MA: Twayne Publishers, 1982.

Blyth, R.H., Translator. *Haiku: Volume 1,2, 3, 4, Eastern Culture.* Tokyo, Japan: Hokuseido Press, 1949. Twenty-third printing, 1976.

Braida, Darold D., Editor. *The Anthology of Hawaii Education Association Haiku Award Winners 1977-1979.* Honolulu, HI: Hawaii Education Association, 1979.

British Haiku Society. *Haiku Kit: A Teaching Pack, Second Edition.* Braintree, Essex, UK: British Haiku Society, 1998.

Brooks, Randy. *The Art of Reading and Writing Haiku: A Reader Response Approach.* Taylorville, IL: Brooks Books, 2019.

Brooks, Randy. *Centennial High School Haiku Cut. Online edition.* Decatur, IL: Millikin University, 2007. <http://www.brooksbookshaiku.com/MillikinHaiku/competitions/CentennialHighSchool/>

Brooks, Randy. *2010 Centennial High School Haiku Cut. Online edition.* Decatur, IL: Millikin University, 2010. <http://www.brooksbookshaiku.com/ MillikinHaiku/competitions/CentennialHighSchool2010>

Brooks, Randy. *Haiku Writing & Editing. Online edition.* Prairieland Advocates for Gifted Children, Decatur, IL: Millikin University, 1999. < http://www. brooksbookshaiku.com/MillikinHaiku/haiku/pagchaiku>

Brooks, Randy, Editor. Jennifer Griebel, Art Editor. *Harristown Haiku Anthology: Harristown Elementary School Students. Online edition.* Decatur, IL: Millikin University, 2003. <http://www.brooksbookshaiku.com/MillikinHaiku/ HarristownHaikuWeb/titlepage.html>

Brooks, Randy & Emily Evans, Melanie McLay, Rick Bearce, Editors. *Millikin University Haiku Anthology.* Decatur, IL: Bronze Man Books, October 2008.

Brooks, Randy, Editor. Warrensburg-Latham *Haiku Workshop Anthology: Haiku by Sixth Graders. Online edition.* Decatur, IL: Brooks Books, 1998. <http:// www.brooksbookshaiku.com/wlhaiku>.

Burns, Allan, Editor. *Where the River Goes: The Nature Tradition in English-Language Haiku.* Ormisk, UK: Snap Shot Press, 2013.

Burns, Molly. *Haiku Unit Plan for Secondary Education. Online edition.* Decatur, IL: Millikin University, 2005. <http://www.brooksbookshaiku. com/MillikinHaiku/courses/globalSpring2005/HaikuUnitPlan/ MollyBurnsUnitPlan.html>

Buson, Yosa. Edited and translated by Edith Marcombe Shiffert and Yuki Sawa. *Haiku Master Buson: Translations from the Writings of Yosa Buson—Poet and Artist—With Related Materials.* Buffalo, NY: White Pine Press, 2007. [Reprint of 1978 edition.]

Calkins, Jean, Editor. *Handbook on Haiku, Patterned Poems and Articles, Volume 2.* Kanona, NY: J & C Transcripts, 1972.

Carter, Terry Ann, Editor. *Lighting the Global Lantern: A Teacher's Guide to Writing Haiku and Related Literary Forms.* Township of South Frontenac, Ontario, Canada: Wintergreen Studios Press, 2011.

Cobb, David, Editor. *Tadpoles: Haiku by British School Children.* Shalford, Essex, UK: British Haiku Society, 1999.

Corman, Cid, translator. *Born of a Dream: 50 Haiku by Basho, Buson, Taigi, Issa, Shiki.* Frankfort, KY: Gnomon.

Deodhar, Angelee, Editor. *Children's Haiku from Around the World: A Haiku Primer.* Chandigarh, India: Azad Hind Stores, Ltd., 2007. [Hindi & English.]

Digregorio, Charlotte. *Haiku and Senryu: A Simple Guide for All.* Winnetka, IL: Artful Communicators Press, 2014.

Donegan, Patricia. *Haiku: Asian Arts & Crafts for Creative Kids*. Rutland, VT: Charles E. Tuttle Company, 2003.

Donegan, Patricia. *Haiku Mind: 108 Poems to Cultivate Awareness and Open Your Heart*. Boston, MA: Shambala, 2008.

Drevniok, Betty. *Aware—A Haiku Primer*. Bellingham, WA: Portals Publications, 1981.

Gilbert, Richard and David Ostman. *Earth in Sunrise: A Course for English-Language Study*. Winchester, VA: Red Moon Press, 2017.

Gurga, Lee. *Haiku: A Poet's Guide*. Lincoln, IL: Modern Haiku Press, 2003.

Gurga, Lee and Scott Metz. *Haiku 21: An Anthology of Contemporary English-language Haiku*. Lincoln, IL: Modern Haiku Press, 2011.

Haiku Society of America Twentieth Anniversary Book Committee. *A Haiku Path: The Haiku Society of America 1968-1988*. New York: Haiku Society of America, 1994.

Haiku Society of America Education Committee. *Haiku Resources Packet for Teachers, 2nd Edition*. New York: Haiku Society of America, 1999. [Includes *British Haiku Society Teacher's Kit, Frogpond 22.2, Haiku Compass, The Classic Tradition of Haiku Anthology,* and *The Haiku Habit Workshop.*]

Harter, Penny. *Shadow Play: Night Haiku*. New York: Simon & Schuster, 1994.

Henderson, Harold G. *Haiku in English*. Rutland, VT: Charles E. Tuttle Co., 1967.

Higginson, William J. *The Haiku Handbook: How to Write, Share, and Teach Haiku*. New York: Kodansha International, 1985.

Issa, Kobayashi. Translated by David G. Lanoue. *Issa, Cup of Tea Poems: Selected Haiku of Kobayashi Issa*. Berkeley, CA: Asian Humanities Press, 1991.

Issa, Kobayashi. Translated by Lewis Mackenzie. *The Autumn Wind: A Selection from the Poems of Issa*. London: John Murray (Publishers) Ltd, 1957.

Japan Air Lines Foundation. *Haiku by the Children '90*. Japan: JAL Foundation, 1991. [Anthology of best selections from the 1990 Japan Air Lines World Children's Haiku Contest '90.]

Japan Air Lines Foundation. *Haiku by the Children*. Japan: JAL Foundation, 1995. [Anthology of best selections from the 1994 Japan Air Lines World Children's Haiku contest.]

Japan Project. *The Haiku Moment: Seeing the World in a Grain of Sand*. A curriculum unit for elementary levels developed by The Japan Project, Stanford Program on International and Cross-cultural Education (SPICE). Originally developed by Kay Sandberg Abe and revised in 1995 by Jocelyn Young. Stanford, CA: Stanford University, 1995. Includes cassette audio tape and slide show.

Kacian, Jim, Editor with Philip Rowland and Allan Burns. *Haiku in English: The First Hundred Years*. New York: W. W. Norton & Company, 2013.

Kondo, Kris. *Renku in the Classroom: A Case for Introducing International Renku into College English Classes in Japan*. [Reprint monograph from a Japanese magazine.] 1996.

Lanoue, David G. *Haiku Guy*. Winchester, VA: Red Moon Press, 2000.

Latham, Jessica Malone, Editor. *Another Trip Around the Sun: 365 Days of Haiku for Children Young and Old*. Taylorville, IL: Brooks Books, 2019.

Mason, Scott, Editor. *The Wonder Code: Discover the Way of Haiku and See the World with New Eyes*. Chappaqua, NY: Girasole Press, 2017.

Reichhold, Jane. *Writing and Enjoying Haiku: A Hands-on Guide*. Tokyo, New York, London: Kodansha International, 2002.

Root-Bernstein, Michele and Francine Banwarth. *The Haiku Life: What We Learned as Editors of Frogpond*. Lincoln, IL: Modern Haiku Press, 2017.

Ross, Bruce, Editor. *Haiku Moment: An Anthology of Contemporary North American Haiku*. Rutland, VT: Charles E. Tuttle Company, 1993.

Ross, Bruce. *How to Haiku: A Writer's Guide to Haiku and Related Forms*. Rutland, VT: Charles E. Tuttle Company, 2002.

Ueda, Makoto, *Bashô and His Interpreters: Selected Hokku with Commentary*. Stanford, CA: Stanford University Press, 1992.

Ueda, Makoto, *Matsuo Bashô*. Tokyo & New York: Kodansha International LTD., 1982.

Ueda, Makoto. Editor and translator. *Modern Japanese Haiku: An Anthology*. Toronto: University of Toronto Press, 1976.

Van Kirk, Geoffrey, Kazuo Tsuda, and Mami Masuya Fleming, Editors. *2014 Student Haiku Contest: A Poetic Competition for Students and Their Teachers in Elementary, Middle and High School writing in English or Japanese*. New York: The United Nations International School, 2014.

Van den Heuvel, Cor, Editor. *The Haiku Anthology, Expanded Edition*. New York: W.W. Norton, 1999.

Virgilio, Nicholas. *Nick Virgilio: A Life in Haiku*. Edited by Raffael de Gruttola. Arlington, VA: Turtle Light Press, 2012.

Virgilio, Nicholas A. *Selected Haiku*. Sherbrooke, P.Q.: Burnt Lake Press, 1985.

Wakan, Naomi Beth. *The Way of Haiku*. Brunswick, ME: Shanti Arts Publishing, 2019.

Yamaguchi, Tazuo & Randy Brooks, Editors. *Haiku: The Art of the Short Poem*. Film by Tazuo Yamaguchi on DVD. Decatur, IL: Brooks Books, 2008.

Yasuda, Kenneth. *A Pepper-Pod: A Haiku Sampler*. Rutland, VT: Charles E. Tuttle, 1976. (Reprint of the 1947 first edition published by Alfred A. Knopf.)

Recommended Articles and Theses

Alston, Linda. "Teaching Haiku to Young Children." *NAMTA Journal* (North American Montessori Teachers' Association) 18.2 (1993): 43-50.

Arntzen, Sonja and Janice Brown. "Old Pond, Students Leap in, Sound of Laughter: Creative Projects in the Teaching of Japanese Classical Literature." *Japanese Language and Literature* 35.1 (2001): 17-36.

Blasko, Dawn G., and Dennis W. Merski. "Haiku Poetry and Metaphorical Thought: An Invitation to Interdisciplinary Study." *Creativity Research Journal* 11.1 (1998): 39-46.

Brooks, Randy. "Language Arts Books on Teaching Haiku." *Haiku Review '87* (1987): 48-57.

Brooks, Randy. "Teaching Haiku at Millikin University." *Riverbed Haiku* 1.2 (2008): 35-38.

Brooks, Randy. "Teaching Haiku in American Higher Education." *Dust Devils: The Red Moon Anthology of English-Language Haiku 2016.* Winchester, VA: Red Moon Press, (2017): 121-146.

Brooks, Randy. "Teaching Haiku in Higher Education: An Immersion into the Living Tradition—the Case of Millikin University." *World Haiku Review* 1.3 (2001).

Cherner, Anne. "Haiku—the Discipline of Language." *Teachers and Writers Magazine* 12.2 (1981): 14-16.

DeVito, Becky. "Writing as Inquiry: How Might the Practice of Writing Poetry Function as an Epistemic Tool for Poets?" Harvard University, 2010. Dissertation. 372 pages.

Dufort Shirlee Perazzo. "Haiku Evolutions and a Fresh Rationale for Creating Collaboration, Connection and Community in the College Classroom." State University of New York at Albany, 2008. Dissertation. 161 pages.

Ellman, Neil. "Haiku and Photography: Literary Interpretation and Visual Literacy." *Journal of English Teaching Techniques* 9.1-2 (1976): 6-10.

Fidyk, Alexandra, and Jason Wallin. "The Daimon, The Scarebird and Haiku: Repeated Narrations." *Journal of Curriculum and Pedagogy* 2.2 (2005): 215-243.

Friedland, Ellie. "Look and Look Again: A Heuristic Inquiry into Education as Awareness." The Union Institute, 1994. Dissertation. 184 pages.

Gabauer, George. "In the Shortness of a Breath… Haiku and Nature Interpretation." *Journal of Outdoor Education* 19 (1984-85): 25-27.

Gair, Susan. "Haiku as A Creative Writing Approach to Explore Empathy with Social Work Students: A Classroom-Based Inquiry." *Journal of Poetry Therapy: The*

Interdisciplinary Journal of Practice, Theory, Research, And Education 25.2
(2012): 69-82.

Gaire, Denise B. "How a Haiku Project Stimulated Poetry Reading among Elementary
Students." *Library Media Connection* 22.4 (2004): 41-42.

Genovese, Pete. "Overview of Japanese Poetry. Asian Studies Instructional
Module." [Syllabus overview available on ERIC: ED407962]. Saint Louis
Community College at Meramac, MO, 1997.

Greenway, William and Betty Greenway. "Meeting the Muse: Teaching Contemporary
Poetry by Teaching Poetry Writing." *Children's Literature Association
Quarterly* 15.3 (1990): 138-142.

Higginson, William J. "Japanese Poems for American School Kids? Or Why and
How to Not Teach Haiku." *The Whole Word Catalogue* 2. 46-53. New York:
McGraw Hill, 1977.

Hudson, Zach. "Haiku in The Classroom: More Than Counting Syllables." *English
Journal* 102.6 (2013): 54-57.

Iida, Atsushi. "Developing Voice by Composing Haiku: A Social-Expressivist
Approach for Teaching Haiku Writing in EFL Contexts." *English Teaching
Forum* 48.1 (2010): 28-34.

Iida, Atsushi. "Poetry Writing as Expressive Pedagogy in An EFL Context: Identifying
Possible Assessment Tools for Haiku Poetry in EFL Freshman College
Writing." *Assessing Writing* 13.3 (2008): 171-179.

Iida, Atsushi. "Revisiting Haiku: The Contribution of Composing Haiku to L2
Academic Literacy Development." Indiana University of Pennsylvania,
2011. Dissertation. 216 pages.

Kenny, Adele. "The Haiku Connection." *Teachers and Writers Magazine* 12.2 (1981):
12-13.

McDonald, Nan L., & Douglas Fisher. "Haiku: Active Learning with and through the
Arts." *Teaching Literacy through the Arts.* Guilford Publications, 2006.

Nakajima, K. "Research on the haiku poems creation method of instruction
according to development process." *Bulletin of Hokuriku Gakuin Junior
College* 40 (2008): 33-42. National Endowment for the Humanities.
The world of haiku, 2000. Education Resources Information Center:
<http://www.eric.ed.gov/ERICDocs/data/ericdocs2sql/content_
storage_01/0000019b/80/16/d1/e7.pdf>.

Parks, Mary. "Integrate Art! Match Poetry to Painting." *Instructor* 104.4 (1994): 30.

Rielly, Edward J. "Reading and Writing Haiku in The Classroom." *Children's Literature
Association Quarterly* 13.3 (1988): 111-114.

Rillero, Peter. "Haiku and Science—Observing, Reflecting, and Writing About
Nature." *Journal of College Science Teaching* 28.5 (1999): 345-347.

Root-Bernstein, Michele. "Haiku as Emblem of Creative Discovery: Another Path to Craft." *Modern Haiku* 41.3 (2010): 16-25.

Stanford University Program on International and Cross-Cultural Education. The Haiku Moment: Seeing the World in a Grain of Sand. A Curriculum Unit for Elementary Levels. Revised. Stanford University, CA: 1995. [25 pages]

Stanford University Program on International and Cross-Cultural Education. The Haiku Moment: Seeing the World in a Grain of Sand. A Curriculum Unit for Secondary Levels. Revised. Stanford University, CA: 1995. [42 pages]

Stephenson, Kittredge Taylor. "Extending the Writing Paradigm: Is Writing Haiku Poetry Healing?" Texas A&M University, 2009. MA thesis in psychology. 37 pages.

Stephenson, Kittredge and David H. Rosen. "Haiku and Healing: An Empirical Study of Poetry Writing as Therapeutic and Creative Intervention." *Empirical Studies in the Arts* 33.1 (2015): 36-60.

Stephenson, Kittredge Taylor. "Haiku, Nature, and Narrative: An Empirical Study of the Writing Paradigm and Its Theories." Texas A&M University, 2014. Dissertation.

Vakar, Anna. "Some Thoughts on Teaching Haiku in the Schools." *Frogpond* 2.3-4 (1979): 11-14.

Van den Heuvel, Cor, Editor. *The Haiku Anthology.* 3rd Edition. Garden City, NY: Anchor Books, 1974.

Wamboldt, Helen Jane. "Haiku as a Tool in Teaching Oral Interpretation." *Speech Teacher* 13.3 (1964): 171-175.

Whittingham, Jeff L. "Haiku: Teaching the Art of Brevity in Writing." *Childhood Education* 80.1 (2003): 25-28.

Wilson, Robert. "An Interview with Professor Randy Brooks." *Simply Haiku* 9.2 (2011).

Wyvell, Mary L. "American Haiku: A Classroom Experiment." *Improving College and University Teaching* 21.2 (1973): 135-136.

Yahnke, Robert. "Teaching Haiku Poetry in the Humanities Classroom." *Improving College and University Teaching* 29.2 (1981): 71-77.

Yanagihara, Y. "Choosing expressions by group discussion and improving the understanding of the words: To prove the attraction of words through making haiku (Japanese course the third grade of junior high school)." *Educational Research Bulletin of Fukui University* 32 (2007): 69-75.

Zolbrod, Leon. "Teaching Haikai: The Case of 'Peonies Scatter.'" *Frogpond* 2.3/4 (1979): 32-35.

Print Magazines and Journals

Acorn. A.C. Missias, Editor. Philadelphia, PA: Redfox Press; 1998-2008. Carolyn Hall, Editor. San Francisco, CA; 2008-2012. Susan Antolin, Editor. San Francisco, CA; 2012-2020.

Blithe Spirit: Journal of the British Haiku Society. Caroline Gourlay, Editor. Knighton, Powys, UK: British Haiku Society, 1998-2020.

Bottle Rockets. Stanford M. Forrester, Editor. Wethersfield, CT: 1999-2020.

Frogpond. Haiku Society of America. Lilli Tanzer, Editor. Hopewell Junction, NY; 1978-1980. Geoffrey O'Brien, Editor. New York, NY; 1981. Bruce Kennedy, Editor. Brooklyn, NY; 1982-1983. Alexis Rotella, Editor. Mountain Lakes, NJ; 1983-1984. Elizabeth Searle Lamb, Editor. Santa Fe, NM; 1984-1990. Sylvia Forges-Ryan, Editor. North Haven, CT; 1991-1993. Elizabeth Searle Lamb, Editor. Santa Fe, NM; 1994. Kenneth C. Leibman, Editor. Archer, FL; 1995-1997. Jim Kacian, Editor. Winchester, VA; 1998-2004. John Stevenson, Editor. Nassau, NY; 2005-2007. George Swede, Editor. Toronto, Canada; 2008-2012. Francine Banwarth, Editor. Dubuque, IA; 2012-2015. Aubrie Cox, Editor. Knoxville, TN; 2016. Christopher Patchel, Editor. Libertyville, IL; 2016-2018. Michael Ketchek, Editor. Rochester, NY; 2018-2020.

Gusts: Contemporary Tanka. Kozue Uzawa, Editor. Lethbridge, AB, Canada: Tanka Canada; 2007-2020.

Heron's Nest. Christopher Herold, Editor. Port Townsend, WA, and John Stevenson, Editor; 1999-2020.

Juxtapositions: A Journal of Haiku Research and Scholarship. Peter McDonald, Senior Editor. Stephen Addiss, Randy M. Brooks, Bill Cooper, Aubrie Cox, Editors. Winchester, VA: The Haiku Foundation; 2015-2020.

Mayfly. Randy & Shirley Brooks, Editors. Battleground, IN, Decatur, IL, and Taylorville, IL; 1986-2020.

Modern Haiku. Kay Titus Mormino, Editor. San Clemente, CA; 1970-1977. Robert Spiess, Editor. Madison, WI; 1978-2002. Lee Gurga, Editor. Lincoln, IL; 2002-2006. Charles Trumbull, Editor. Evanston, IL & Santa Fe, NM; 2006-2013. Paul Miller, Editor. Portsmouth, RI; 2013-2020.

Noon: Journal of the Short Poem. Philip Rowland, Editor. Tokyo: Noon Press; 2005-2020.

Ribbons: Tanka Society of America Journal. An'ya, Editor. Crescent, OR; 2005-2007. Dave Bacharach, Editor. Alpine, NY; 2007-2011. David Rice, Editor. Berkeley, CA; 2012-2020.

Online Resources

Anonymous. "Haiku: Lesson Plan for Teachers, Grades 6-12" and "Haiku: Lesson Plan for Teachers, Grades 1-5." Haiku Society of America, (2012): n. pag. Web. 2 April 2016.

Bennett, Brad. "Lesson Plan for Grades 3-4." Winchester, VA: The Haiku Foundation, (no date). Web. 26 April 2016. [PDF files including lesson plan and six supplement handouts.]

British Haiku Society. *Haiku Kit: A Teaching Pack,* Second Edition. British Haiku Society, (no date): n. pag. Web. 10 April 2016.

Brooks, Randy and Cynthia Helms. "Centennial High School Haiku Cut." Global Haiku Traditions, Millikin University, (2007). Web. 1 April 2016.

Brooks, Randy, Web Editor. "Haiku Society of America Educational Resources." Haiku Society of America, (2012): n. pag. Web. 1 April 2016.

Brooks, Randy and Jennifer Griebel, Editors. *Harristown Haiku Anthology: Haiku and Haiga by Harristown Elementary School Students.* Global Haiku Traditions, Millikin University, (2003). Web. 1 April 2016.

Brooks, Randy. "Hartsburg-Emden High School April Fool's Matching Contest and Kukai." Global Haiku Traditions, Millikin University, (2011). Web. 1 April 2016.

Brooks, Randy. "Prairieland Advocates for Gifted Children: Haiku Writing & Editing Workshop." Global Haiku Traditions, Millikin University, (1999). Web. 1 April 2016.

Brooks, Randy and Cynthia Helms. "2010 Centennial High School Haiku Cut." Global Haiku Traditions, Millikin University, (2010). Web. 1 April 2016.

Brooks, Randy, Editor. *Warrensburg-Latham Middle School Haiku Anthology.* Decatur, IL: Brooks Books, (1998). Web. 1 April 2016.

Burns, Molly. *Haiku Unit Plan for Secondary Education.* Global Haiku Traditions, Millikin University, (2005): n. pag. Web. 1 April 2016.

Cobb, David, Editor. *Tadpoles: Haiku by British School Children.* British Haiku Society, (1999). The Haiku Foundation Digital Library. Web. 3 May 2016.

DeVito, Becky. "Writing as Inquiry: How might the practice of writing poetry function as an epistemic tool for poets?" Cambridge, MA: Harvard University (2010). Dissertation. 362 pages. The Haiku Foundation Digital Library. Web. 27 January 2017.

Dougherty, Sean, Video Editor. "Remembering Nick Virgilio." Winchester, VA: *The Haiku Foundation,* (2015). Web. 23 April 2016. [Video.]

Drevniok, Betty. *Aware: A Haiku Primer.* Bellingham, WA: Portal Publications, (1981). *The Haiku Foundation Digital Library.* Web. 4 May 2016.

Greve, Gabi. "Basic Haiku Theories: Haiku Lessons." World Kigo Database (WKD). Daruma Museum, Japan, (2000). Web. 12 April 2016.

Grubb, Rebecca, Editor. "Traditional Haiku Meets Urban-Life Senryu." Nick Virgilio Poetry Project, Rutgers University. Camden, New Jersey (2016). [Web site.] Web. 28 March 2017.

Haiku Kit, 2nd Edition. British Haiku Society, (no date). Web 15 April 2016. [A teaching pack that meets the requirements of Keystage 3 in the English Section of the National Curriculum.]

Hartman, Tom, Editor. Nick Virgilio Poetry Project, Rutgers University. Camden, New Jersey. [Web site.] Web. 28 March 2017.

"The Archive: Virgilio's Unpublished Work." Nick Virgilio Poetry Project, Rutgers University. Camden, New Jersey. [Web site.] Web. 28 March 2017. "Sample Drafts." Nick Virgilio Poetry Project, Rutgers University. Camden, New Jersey (2016). [Web site.] Web. 28 March 2017.

Higginson, William J. "Guidelines for Writing Haiku." Winchester, VA: The Haiku Foundation, (2003). Web. 26 April 2016.

Isaacson, Helen Shigeko. "Children's Haiku." (2010). The Haiku Foundation Digital Library. Web. 11 May 2016. [Unpublished manuscript.]

Kacian, Jim. *A Dozen Tongues 2000: Children's Haiku from Around the World.* Winchester, VA: Red Moon Press, (2000). The Haiku Foundation Digital Library. Web. 13 May 2016.

Kacian, Jim and Ellen Grace Olinger, Web Editors. "Education Resources." Winchester, VA: The Haiku Foundation, (2008-2015). Web. 26 April 2016. [Includes: Lessons for Kindergarten, 1st-2nd grades, 3rd-4th grades, 5th-6th grades, Junior High School, High School and Higher Education.]

Kacian, Jim. *How to Haiku.* Winchester, VA: Red Moon Press, (2006). The Haiku Foundation Digital Library. Web. 13 May 2016.

Kei, M., Editor. *25 Tanka for Children (and Educators).* Perryville, MD: Keibooks, (2011). Web. 1 April 2016.

Kondo, Tadashi Shokan, and William J. Higginson. "Link and Shift: A Practical Guide to Renku Composition." Haikai Home, (2003): n. pag. Web. 12 April 2016.

Lipkewich, A. E. and R. S. Mazurenko, Web Editors. *Bringing Haiku Back to Life: Grade 7 PowerPoint Mini-Poetry Unit.* Edmonton, Canada: Westmont School, Edmonton Public Schools, (1999). Web. 19 April 2016.

Martin, Jeannie. "Thoughts on Teaching and Learning Haiku." Haiku Society of America, (2012): n. pag. Web. 2 April 2016.

Painting, Tom. "Haiku Challenge 1, 2, 3, 4." Winchester, VA: The Haiku Foundation, (no date). Web. 26 April 2016.

Painting, Tom, Teacher and Moderator. "A Reading by the Paideia School." Winchester, VA: The Haiku Foundation, (2013). Web. 23 April 2016. [YouTube Video.]

Painting, Tom. "What's Lurking? Haiku Workshop Exercise." Winchester, VA: The Haiku Foundation, (no date). Web. 26 April 2016.

Painting, Tom. "Workshop: Haiku and Imagery." Haiku Society of America, (2012): n. pag. Web. 2 April 2016.

Painting, Tom. "Workshop: How to Haiku." Haiku Society of America, (2012): n. pag. Web. 2 April 2016.

Painting, Tom. "Workshop: Kigo and Seasonality in Haiku." Haiku Society of America, (2012): n. pag. Web. 2 April 2016.

Painting, Tom. "Workshop: Narrative Thinking." Haiku Society of America, (2012): n. pag. Web. 2 April 2016.

Pizzarelli, Alan and Donna Beaver, Podcast Hosts. *Haiku Chronicles,* 1-32. Bloomfield, NJ, (2009-2016). Web. 19 April 2016. [Pocast available from iTunes.]

"Q&A with Global Haiku Students from Millikin University." *Haiku Chronicles,* 11. Bloomfield, NJ, (2010). Web. 19 April 2016. [Audio.]

Raine, Katherine. *Learning to Write Haiku: A Teacher's Guide.* New Zealand Poetry Society, (2016): 47 pages. Web. 13 July 2016.

Reichhold, Jane. *Bare Bones School of Haiku.* Gualala, CA: AHA Poetry, (2012). Web. 1 April 2016.

Reichhold, Jane. *Wind Five-Folded School of Tanka.* Gualala, CA: AHA Poetry, (2011). Web. 1 April 2016.

Tremblay, Jessica. *Advice for Haiku Writers.* Old Pond Comics, (2015). Web. 16 April 2016.

Tremblay, Jessica. *Haiku Lessons.* Old Pond Comics, (2014). Web. 16 April 2016.

Links to these online resources (search if URLs have changed):

AHA Poetry (and AHA Online Books) <http://www.ahapoetry.com/>

Atlas Poetica (Keibooks) <http://atlaspoetica.org/>

British Haiku Society <http://britishhaikusociety.org.uk/>

Haikai Home <http://www.2hweb.net/haikai/main.html>

Haiku Chronicles: A Poetry Podcast <http://www.haikuchronicles.com/>

The Haiku Foundation Digital Library <http://www.thehaikufoundation.org/>

Haiku Society of America <https://www.hsa-haiku.org/>

The Heron's Nest <http://www.theheronsnest.com/> <http://www.haikupoet.com/nest/>

Millikin University Haiku <http://www.brooksbookshaiku.com/MillikinHaiku/>

New Zealand Poetry Society <http://www.poetrysociety.org.nz/>

Nick Virgilio Poetry Project <http://nickvirgilio.camden.rutgers.edu/>

Old Pond Comics <http://www.oldpondcomics.com/>

World Kigo Database <http://worldkigodatabase.blogspot.com/>

Additional Web Resource Links (search if URLs have changed)::

Africa Haiku Network <https://africahaikunetwork.wordpress.com>

Alaska Haiku Society <http://home.gci.net/~alaskahaiku/index.html>

American Haiku Archives <https://www.americanhaikuarchives.org/>

Bones: Journal for Contemporary Haiku <http://www.bonesjournal.com/>

Brooks Books <http://www.brooksbookshaiku.com/>

Cattails <http://www.unitedhaikuandtankasociety.com/>

Chrysanthemum (Bregengemme) <http://www.bregengemme.net/>

Eucalypt <http://www.eucalypt.info/>

Failed Haiku <https://failedhaiku.wordpress.com/>

Graceguts <http://www.graceguts.com/>

Haibun Today <http://haibuntoday.com/>

Haigaonline <http://www.haigaonline.com/>

Haiku Canada <http://www.haikucanada.org/>

Haiku International Association <http://www.haiku-hia.com/index_en.html>

Haiku Northwest <https://sites.google.com/site/haikunorthwest/>

Haiku Oz: The Australian Haiku Society <http://www.haikuoz.org/>

Juxtapositions <http://www.thehaikufoundation.org/juxta/>

Living Haiku Anthology <http://livinghaikuanthology.com/>

Modern Haiku <https://www.modernhaiku.org/>

North Carolina Haiku Society <http://nc-haiku.org/>

Nick Virgilio Haiku Association <https://www.nickvirgiliohaiku.org/>

Nick Virgilio Poetry Project <http://nickvirgilio.camden.rutgers.edu/>

Prune Juice <https://prunejuice.wordpress.com/>

SciFaiKu.com Science Fiction Haiku <http://www.scifaiku.com/>

Shamrock <http://shamrockhaiku.webs.com/>

The Mamba Journal <https://africahaikunetwork.wordpress.com/contact/>

Tinywords <http://tinywords.com/>

Under the Basho <http://underthebasho.com/>

Wild Plum <https://wildplumhaiku.wordpress.com/>

World Haiku Review <https://sites.google.com/site/worldhaikureview2/>

Yuki Teikei Haiku Society <https://youngleaves.org/>

Bibliography Formats:

Author, First Name. *Title of the Book.* Place: Publisher, date.

Author, First Name. Translator. *Title of the Book.* Place: Publisher, date.

Title of the Magazine. Editor. Place: Publisher, issues; dates.

MLA online citation formats:

Author, First. *Book Title.* City, State: Publisher, (year). Web. date month year(viewed).

Author, First. "Exhibition title." Web Site, (year): n. pag. Web. date month year(viewed).

Author, First. "Exhibition title." Course, University (year): n. pag. Web. date month year(viewed).

Last, First, Editor. *OnlineJournalTitle.* xx.x – xx.x, Publisher, (year – year). Web. date month year(viewed).

Print Articles and Theses on Nick Virgilio

Black, Rick. "Nick Virgilio, Walt Whitman, and the American Poetic Tradition: An Interview with Kwame Dawes." *Frogpond: The Journal of the Haiku Society of America* 38:1, (2015), 99-112.

Clausen, Tom. "Nick Virgilio, My Haiku Hero." *Frogpond: The Journal of the Haiku Society of America* 35.2, (2012), 87-93.

Litchfield, Electus D. "Yorkship Village." *The American Review of Reviews* 6 (Dec. 1919), 599-602.

McClintock, Michael. "The Camden Elegist [Nicholas Virgilio]." *Modern Haiku* 4.3, (1973): 7-12.

Moser, Elizabeth Sands. "Looking Past the Lily: Layers of Meaning and Interconnectivity in Nick Virgilio's Haiku." Rutgers, the State University of New Jersey, 2012. MA thesis in English, 49 pages.

O'Toole, Kathleen, Charles D. Nethaway, Jr., and Marty Moss-Cohane. "In Memory of Nicholas Virgilio: Out of the Water." *A Haiku Path: The Haiku Society of America* 1968-1988. New York: Haiku Society of America, 1994.

Philadelphia Inquirer, "Renowned Camden poet Nicholas Virgilio, 60, dies in Washington," (January 4, 1989), B1.

Robinson, Michele. "Japanese and American Influences on Poetic Form and Content in Nicholas A. Virgilio's Haiku." Rutgers University, 2004. Dissertation.

Sexton, John W. "Aural Experience: Sound and Rhythm in The Haiku of Nicholas A. Virgilio." *Frogpond: The Journal of The Haiku Society of America* 32.1 (2009): 66-72.

Van den Heuvel, Cor. "Nicholas Virgilio and the End of Innocence." *Frogpond: The Journal of The Haiku Society of America* 12:2, (1989), 28-30.

Virgilio, Nicholas. "An Unknown Flower." *Leatherneck* 51:3, (March 1968), 89.

Online Articles and Resources on Nick Virgilio

Ade, Lori. "Nicholas Virgilio's Haiku of Passion." Millikin University Haiku, (2004). <http://www.brooksbookshaiku.com/MillikinHaiku/writerprofiles/AdeOnVirgilio.html>

Black, Rick. "Rediscovering a Lost Voice: Nick Virgilio." *Notes from the Gean* 13, (2012): 101-105. <https://www.thehaikufoundation.org/omeka/files/original/bd749b6be502cbd0590736a8ff323570.pdf>

Bronke, Christopher. "Nicholas Virgilio: Haiku Makes the Man." Millikin University Haiku, (2003). <http://www.brooksbookshaiku.com/MillikinHaiku/writerprofiles/BronkeOnVirgilio.html>

Doyle, Michael. "Father Michael Doyle on Haiku Poet Nick Virgilio." *Discover Jersey Arts Culture Vultures,* (June 11, 2012). [Audio.] <https://jerseyartsfeatures.com/content/index.php/nj-podcasts/2012/06/father-michael-doyle-on-haiku-poet-nick-virgilio-and-how-the-arts-are-saving-camde>

Dougherty, Sean, Video Editor. "Remembering Nick Virgilio." Camden, NJ, (July 26, 2009). [Video.] <https://www.youtube.com/watch?v=wjq6TmbTabc>

Housh, Kathy. "Nicholas A. Virgilio: Vietnam War Haiku." Millikin University Haiku, (2015). <http://www.brooksbookshaiku.com/MillikinHaiku /courses/globalPACEsept2015/KathyHoushOnVirgilio.html>

Mudd, Rachel. "Nicholas Virgilio: Haiku of Emotions." Millikin University Haiku (2013). <http://www.brooksbookshaiku.com/MillikinHaiku/courses/globalFall2013/RachelMuddOnVirgilio.html>

Nick Virgilio Haiku Association <https://www.nickvirgiliohaiku.org/>

Nick Virgilio. The Living Haiku Anthology. <https://livinghaikuanthology.com/index-of-poets/livinglegacies/2647-nick-virgilio.html>

Nick Virgilio Poetry Project, Rutgers University. Camden, New Jersey. [Web site.] <http://nickvirgilio.camden.rutgers.edu/>

"The Archive: Virgilio's Unpublished Work." Nick Virgilio Poetry Project, Rutgers University. Camden, New Jersey. <https://nickvirgilio.camden.rutgers.edu/poems/unpublished_materials/>

"Sample Drafts." Nick Virgilio Poetry Project, Rutgers University. Camden, New Jersey (2016). < https://nickvirgilio.camden.rutgers.edu/poems/drafts/>

Nick Virgilio. Wikipedia. <https://en.wikipedia.org/wiki/Nick_Virgilio>

Nielsen, Bruce. "The Straightforward Haiku of Nicholas A. Virgilio." Millikin University Haiku, (2005). <http://www.brooksbookshaiku.com/

MillikinHaiku/writerprofiles/NielsenOnVirgilio.html>

O'Toole, Kathleen. "*Nick Virgilio (1928-1989): An American Haiku Master Revisited.*" *A Hundred Gourds* 1.4, (2012): n. pag. Web. 10 March 2016.

Pizzarelli, Alan. "Featured Poet: Nicholas A. Virgilio." *Simply Haiku* 7.1 (2009). <http://www.simplyhaiku.com/SHv7n1/senryu/senryuFeature.html>

Russo, Dave. "Remembering Nick Virgilio." North Carolina Haiku Society, (2015). [27-minute version of the original documentary film by Dean Dougherty, 1989.] <https://nc-haiku.org/film-remembering-nick-virgilio/>

Sayles, Dana. "Vietnam War Haiku: A Study of Nick Virgilio." Millikin University Haiku (2013). <http://www.brooksbookshaiku.com/MillikinHaiku/courses/globalPACEjuly2013/saylesOnVirgilio.html>

Smith, Chase. "Nicholas A. Virgilio's Realistic Haiku." Millikin University Haiku (2017). <http://www.brooksbookshaiku.com/MillikinHaiku/courses/globalspring2017/ChaseSmithOnVirgilio.html>

Trethan, Phaedra. "Writers House a Tribute to Camden's Famed Haiku Poet." *The Courier Post* (March 19, 2018). <https://www.courierpostonline.com/story/news/2018/03/19/writers-house-camdens-haiku-poet-nick-virgilio/429360002/>

Van den Heuvel, Cor. "Nick Virgilio and American Haiku: Creating Haiku and an Audience." Camden, NJ: Nick Virgilio Poetry Project, (2002). <https://nickvirgilio.camden.rutgers.edu/scholarship/papers/cor-van-den-heuvel/>

About Nick Virgilio

Born on June 28, 1928, Nicholas Anthony Virgilio lived most of his life in his family's rowhome in the Fairview Village section of Camden, New Jersey. From 1963 until his death, he published over 795 poems, almost all haiku.[1] Besides hundreds of poems published in such magazines as *American Haiku, Frogpond, Asphodel, Cicada, Haiku West,* and *Modern Haiku,* he published two editions of his book, *Selected Haiku,* the first from Burnt Lake Press (1985) and the second from Burnt Lake and Black Moss Presses (1988). He died in Washington D.C. on January 3, 1989, while recording an interview about haiku with Scott Simon who was filling in for Charlie Rose that was to appear later in the day on the CBS-TV program "Nightwatch."[2] He is considered one of the founders of haiku written in the American idiom.[3]

Nick Virgilio was the eldest son of Anthony Virgilio, a violinist, and Rose Alemi Virgilio, a seamstress. His brothers were Anthony ("Tony") and Lawrence ("Larry"). The architect of Fairview Village, Electus Darwin Litchfield, envisioned it as "a place of light rooms and clean yards, with adequate playgrounds and amusement fields; a place of beauty and appropriateness and cleanliness."[4] Something of this ideal of beauty and happiness, surrounded by encroaching urban decay and the sorrow of death, may be found in many of Nick Virgilio's haiku.

After graduating from Camden High School in 1946, Virgilio served two years in the US Navy. He returned to Camden and earned a B.A. degree at Temple University. After spending several years in Texas, he again returned to Camden, where he began a career in radio and sports broadcasting, working with Jerry Blavat, "The Geator with the Heater," at dances and on radio shows. He earned the nickname "Nickaphonic Nick," and developed a wide following as a disc jockey. It was said of him that he was "always willing to jump off the stage and dance if things got too quiet."[5]

Virgilio's career as a radio personality, however, was interrupted in 1962 when he came across a volume of haiku poetry in the stacks of the Rutgers University Library. The book was *A Pepper-Pod: Classic Japanese Poems together with Original Haiku by Shōson* (1946), an anthology of translations of poems by Bashō, Buson, Issa, Shiki, and several other Japanese masters of haiku. The haiku were translated by *"Shōson,"* a pen name for Kenneth Yasuda, who appended 59 of his own haiku in a section that he called "Experiments in English." The book was literally an experiment to see if the Japanese form, consisting of a line of seventeen sound units, could be adapted for use in English. Yasuda divided the sound units, or syllables in English, into three lines, of which the first and third were the same length, and the middle line about a third longer. He devised a mathematical formula that defined haiku as "a line of from sixteen to eighteen syllables divided into three parts or lines in such a way that the first is the same length as the third, and one half of the first goes into the second three times, i.e. the three parts are in the approximate relation of 5, 7, and 5 syllables."[6] Nick Virgilio adopted Yasuda's formal definition of haiku, improving on it with the help of Harold G. Henderson's *An Introduction to Haiku* (1958), and abandoned his radio career to devote himself entirely to writing haiku.

Over the next 26 years, Nick Virgilio became a powerful force in the development of American haiku. Some of Virgilio's earliest poems are widely considered to be among his best. His first published haiku appeared in the first issue of *American Haiku* (1.1, 1963), and was subsequently quoted or reprinted in at least ten haiku collections:[7]

> Spring wind frees
> the full moon tangled
> in leafless trees.

This poem follows the Yasuda/Henderson model, in which the first and third lines are rhymed, but it departs from the 5-7-5 syllable count in favor of a 2-3-2 metrical pattern, more typical of English prosody. Virgilio took even greater liberties with the haiku form in his most famous poem, which drew praise from the Crown Prince of Japan:

> Lily:
> out of the water . . .
> out of itself.

The "Lily" poem, which was published in the second issue of *American Haiku* (1.2, 1963) and won first prize in the American Haiku Contest for 1963, had a major impact on the writing of American haiku. The poem has only 11 syllables all told, too few for haiku at the time, but it has a metrical pattern that is consistent with the mathematical proportions of haiku as described by Yasuda and Henderson. The internal punctuation marks, which are sound units in Japanese, slow the poem and give it gravity. More importantly, it paints a "word-picture" of a particular event that compares the lily's material origins with its transcendence of them, eliciting an emotional moment attached to a particular season. The poem is inscribed on Virgilio's podium-shaped grave marker in Harleigh Cemetery in Camden.

Though Virgilio never articulated what form an "American" haiku would take, he thought carefully and wrote about his own poetic practice. In his undated essay "On Haiku in English," printed in *Nick Virgilio: A Life in Haiku,* Virgilio addresses some of the formal questions that generally arise in discussions of haiku. He endorses Harold G. Henderson's definition of haiku as "a record of a moment of emotion in which human nature is somehow linked to all nature."[8] This definition, notes Virgilio, departs from the practice of Bashō, whose haiku were strictly "nature-oriented." Yosa Buson (1716-1784), however, wrote "human-oriented" haiku that could more properly be called senryu, rather than haiku. "This is the best approach to haiku for a Westerner rather than Bashō's 'nature-oriented' manner. To write like Bashō, one must live as he did," writes Virgilio, referring to Bashō's periods of seclusion and wandering. Virgilio's haiku may invoke nature in the form of a season word, but they are often set in an urban environment that challenges or contradicts the natural world. As Cor van den Heuvel says, "Virgilio was like Issa—he could go directly to nature in his haiku but he also had to bring his family and community with him. He intermingled his human relationships with nature and his relationship with nature with his love for human beings."[9]

Virgilio also followed Henderson's advice on some other points that make haiku a distinctive form. Virgilio agrees with Henderson that haiku must refer to "a particular event," one that is "happening 'now'—not in the past" ("On Haiku in English," 108). In Bashō's haiku, a frog jumps into the water of an old pond and makes a splash—that sound is enough to connect us to the universe. In a poem from the school of Buson or Shiki, however, the poet constructs an "imagined reality" with elements that may not be present in the particular event itself. The poet uses a "word-painting technique" to imaginatively compare elements that seem unalike, or that are drawn from the human as well as the natural world, or from the past as well as the present. The juxtaposition of these elements arouses an emotion in the reader based on an imaginative comparison of human and natural elements.

Upon his death in 1989, fourteen boxes of typescripts of his poems, published and unpublished, passed into the hands of his brother Tony Virgilio. With the encouragement of the newly formed Nick Virgilio Haiku Association (NVHA), Tony established a fund for the preservation and wider appreciation of his brother's legacy. Tony entrusted the original typescripts to the English Department at Rutgers University-Camden, where Nick had first encountered haiku poetry, along with a fund to encourage the teaching and writing of haiku. After a series of conferences and seminars, the English department and the Special Collections department of Robeson Library at Rutgers University-Camden collaborated with the NVHA on a plan for the digitization of the Virgilio collection. The digitization project, directed by Special Collections librarian Julie Still, was completed in 2019. The digital collection of Nick Virgilio's unpublished haiku, which it is hoped will provide teachers, scholars, and writers with a valuable resource for their work, may be accessed at <http://collections.libraries.rutgers.edu/Nicholas-virgilio-papers>.

For the last twenty-six years of his life, Nick Virgilio roamed the streets of Fairview and the city of Camden, stopping off at Sacred Heart or at the Elgin Diner to see his friends, or crossing the Delaware on the bus to the Reading Terminal, where he bought fresh produce for people in his neighborhood. He read his latest haiku to friends, saying "What do you think of this one?" He gave readings at the Painted Bride coffee shop in Philadelphia, where he read each poem twice, explaining that "the first time you hear the words, the second time you get the meaning."[10] He also gave readings at the Walt Whitman Center for the Arts and Humanities in Camden, which he had helped to establish and where he was the Poet in Residence. Apart from occasional trips to New York to attend meetings of the Haiku Society of America, of which he was a founding member, he stayed close to his home in Camden, where he wrote haiku on his upright Remington in the basement, cared for his ailing mother, and visited the grave of his brother Larry, who was killed in Vietnam in 1967 and is often memorialized in Nick Virgilio's poems.

~ Geoffrey Sills, Rutgers University

Endnotes

[1] Information in this essay about Virgilio's published haiku was generously provided by Charles Trumbull.

[2] Philadelphia Inquirer, "Renowned Camden poet Nicholas Virgilio, 60, dies in Washington," 01/04/1989, B1.

[3] Cor van den Heuvel, "Nicholas Virgilio and the End of Innocence." Frog Pond xii.2 (May 1989), 28-30.

[4] Litchfield, 599.

[5] Philadelphia Inquirer, 01/04/1989, B6.

[6] Kenneth Yasuda, A Pepper Pod. New York: Alfred A. Knopf, 1947, xxviii-xxix.

[7] Information provided by Charles Trumbull.

[8] Nick Virgilio, "On Haiku in English." A Life in Haiku. Ed. Raffael de Gruttola. Arlington, VA: Turtle Light Press, 2012, 107-10. Virgilio quotes from Harold G. Henderson, Haiku in English. New York: Japan Society, 1965, 9.

[9] Van den Heuvel, 29.

[10] George Vallianos and Henry Brann, members of the Nick Virgilio Haiku Association